THE MIRACLE OF FLIGHT

Marlin Perkins' Wild Kingdom

THE MIRACLE
OF FLIGHT

by Richard Cromer

and the Staff of Don Meier Productions

With an Introduction by Marlin Perkins

Illustrated by Joseph Cellini

Doubleday & Company, Inc., Garden City, New York

Library of Congress Catalog Card Number 68–10112
Printed in the United States of America
First Edition

SCIENTIFIC ADVISERS

Emmet R. Blake
Curator of Birds
Chicago Natural History Museum

Alan H. Cromer
Associate Professor of Physics
Northeastern University

CREDITS

Our appreciation goes to the following persons and institutions for kind permission to use their materials as models for some of the illustrations in this book:

Appleton-Century-Crofts, hypothetical ancestor of birds, p. 78, from Gerhard Heilmann's *The Origin of Birds;* G. Ronald Austing, hawk and hummingbird flight sequence, pp. 68–126; Bird Photographs, Inc., loon swimming under water, p. 121; Chicago Natural History Museum, barbules, p. 50, wing, p. 52, skeleton, p. 85; Houghton Mifflin Company, bone comparison, p. 47, and pectoral muscles, p. 86 from Lois and Louis Darling's *Bird;* Carl B. Koford from National Audubon Society, California condor, p. 70; W. B. Saunders Company, migration diagram, p. 138; the Frank J. Gallon Agency, swan, p. 74.

CONTENTS

Introduction

JUST beyond our crowded pockets of civilization is the Wild Kingdom. Each year we have to travel a little farther to get to it—but it's still waiting there. And we can find it if we approach it quietly enough, so we don't drive its living creatures still farther away.

The Wild Kingdom is many different things. It can be a frozen ice pack torn by one-hundred-mile-an-hour winds, or it can be a sandy beach quietly touched by a gentle surf. It can be the dark floor of a forest that the sun never reaches or a fiery desert almost without shade. It covers the sides of mountains and fills the oceans of the world.

And everywhere in the Wild Kingdom are its living creatures: hummingbirds and rhinos, wildebeests and sloths, large and small creatures, swimmers and runners, climbers and jumpers, timid animals and bold ones. They fill the trees and the water and the land and the air with their cries and their songs and their noises. The Wild Kingdom is full of so many different things—and variety is exciting.

But there's another kind of excitement found in the Wild Kingdom. And that's when we begin to realize that the fabric of life, woven into an endless variety of shapes and forms and colors, contains many similarities. Although each form is unique itself, there are certain likenesses that constantly recur. We hope you'll discover some of these similarities as you read this book. When you look at a feather, you see that it's like nothing else in this whole world except another feather. Or is it? The more you look at it, the more complicated it becomes. Why should anything be shaped just this particular way and no other? Or are there other ways to make a feather, other ways to fly? How is it that birds can fly and you can't? If you had feathers, could you fly? And what is flying?

As you begin to find out about flight, you'll see that it's all mixed up with chemistry and physics, astronomy and biology, meteorology and paleontology. Perhaps, when you finish, you'll realize that this book could just as well have been called "The Miracle of Life." For while it begins by looking at just one part of the Wild Kingdom, it's soon forced to reach out in many more directions.

When you've finished, perhaps you'll understand just a little better how each part of life touches another, how the pieces of the world are related one to the other in so many different ways—some that you already know about, some perhaps that you hadn't thought of yet, and some that are still waiting for someone—perhaps you—to notice for the first time.

Marlin Perkins

Chapter 1

FREEDOM OF FLIGHT

FROM the time man first looked up and saw the birds, he must have envied them their freedom of flight. Long before recorded history, he must have tried to follow them into the air. We know he tried wax and feather wings and wooden paddles. Later he built large cloth bags and filled them with warm air and other gases. In this century he has developed heavier-than-air craft. He now is the conqueror of that free space above the land and water.

The body of man was never designed to fly by itself. Only because man could invent machines has he been able to free himself from the ground. But those machines he made have done more than just imitate birds. Today, man flies higher and faster than the birds. Jets roar overhead, climbing out of sight in seconds; or come whining down, easing their enormous weight noisily toward earth. We can fly across the country or across oceans in a few hours. We can leave the cold and snow

of North America after breakfast and enjoy lunch under the warm tropical sun. Or we can be on the other side of our earth in less than a day.

We live in a time when sonic booms no longer startle us. We have become so used to flight, we don't even turn our eyes to look for the plane that caused such a thunderous explosion. The supersonic plane flies too high, too fast, and is already too far away for us to see.

Still that isn't enough. We read of matter-of-fact preparations for moon flights and rocket probes to other planets. Men train for trips into the dark space beyond our earth as others train to be lawyers and accountants and doctors and teachers. We take all this for granted, yet there are some living persons who can remember when the man flew the first plane at Kitty Hawk.

Rocket engines higher than sky-scrapers stand ready to push us farther and farther into space. And still something about birds fascinates us. Maybe it's because they could fly before we could. Maybe it's because we feel rather clumsy yet in our heavy flying machines, still new at the business of flight. Or maybe it's because we know that birds can do incredible things. Some fly 2,400 miles nonstop across the ocean. Others glide hour after hour without ever flapping their wings.

Perhaps we're fascinated because we can't design a plane that flies as efficiently as a bird. We can't even make an airplane wing as good as a bird's

wing. Men have made many different kinds of wings, even wings whose shape can be changed slightly while in flight. But a single bird's wing is an endless number of shapes. Each flexible feather bends with every movement of the wing through the air and every rush of wind, taking just the proper shape needed for that exact moment in time.

Perhaps birds fascinate us because their internal fires burn hotter than those of most other animals. Their hearts beat faster and they eat more food in proportion to their weight. They need more oxygen, operate at higher temperatures, and wear out faster than most other creatures. They glide, soar, dive, fly forward, brake, turn, bank, reverse their engines, fly backward, or hover in the air. Some dive from a height of one hundred feet into the water, others explode suddenly into the air from the tangle of a forest floor.

Birds seem to know each year when to begin migrating, where to go, and how to get there. They can navigate incredible distances: some make 22,-000-mile round trips each year. They can find their way to particular islands in the middle of the very large and unmarked oceans of our earth. They can find their way in the shimmering heat of the day and they can find their way in the darkness of night. They live in the hottest and the coldest parts of our planet. When we see all these things, is it any wonder that birds fascinate us?

But perhaps birds fascinate us because we know that the flight of a

Looking down at the earth that once held him prisoner, man readies himself for flights to the moon and beyond.

rocket or a jet is somehow related to the flight of a bird. The principles that explain one help us to understand the other. For all things that are able to free themselves from the surface of our earth must operate on certain common principles. They must all overcome the powerful and relentless downward pull of gravity.

Still, being fascinated with flight isn't the same as understanding it. Men have watched birds for thousands of years, but it is only recently that we have learned a little about how birds actually fly. For no matter how carefully we look at a bird in flight, we really can't see how it flies. The mystery of flight remains hidden in the blurred flutter of feathers.

It is easy enough to see that birds flap their wings, but it takes only a little thought to realize that a simple flapping up and down will not move a bird forward or lift it from the ground. Fast lenses and films and high-speed motion picture cameras have, however, allowed men to see things that no one was able to see before. Now when scientists look up at the birds, they have a fairly good idea about how birds have overcome the pull of gravity. And the story of how gravity is overcome is one of the most fascinating in the Wild Kingdom.

Chapter 2

THE RELENTLESS TUG
OF GRAVITY

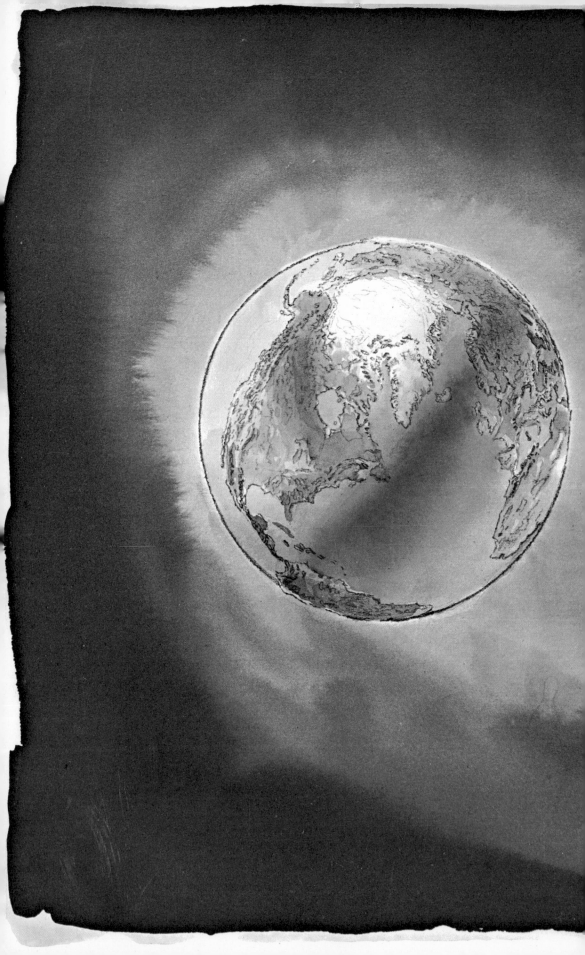

MOVING away from the earth isn't easy, for it seems as though our planet constantly pulls everything toward it. It seems to tug at the moon, pull a hundred tons of interstellar dust down from the sky each day, pull at the air of our planet to keep it from flying off into space, gently return falling leaves to the soil, return each raindrop to the oceans.

It appears to do this because every bit of matter in the universe is attracted to every other bit. The more pieces of matter gathered together, the stronger this attraction becomes. The sun is so large that its pull is great enough to keep the smaller earth orbiting about it in endless loops. The earth is large enough to keep the still smaller moon near it. This is called gravitation.

Gravity and Life

Because our earth is the particular size it is, our gravity is strong enough to keep the air that is so essential for life from drifting off into space. The moon is much smaller and so its gravity is much weaker. Any atmosphere that it might have would escape, and life as we know it is not able to develop on the moon as it did here.

It is possible that some planets are too large and their gravities too strong for life to develop. The giant planets, Jupiter, Saturn, Uranus, and Neptune, have gravities so strong they hold even the light, fast-moving but poisonous gases near them. Earth seems to be just the right size—not too large and not too small. It is large enough to hold the gases necessary for life near it, small enough to have let the life-killing chemicals fly off into space.

Gravity was not only an important factor leading toward the condition in which life as we know it *could* develop here. It has also influenced the shape and size of the living things that *did* develop on this planet (and possibly on other planets in solar systems beyond our own). For gravity pulls on each living thing every moment of its life.

Presumably, life began in the sea. Just when the dead materials of the young planet finally combined into the first living thing, no one knows. It happened far back in the past, perhaps two billion years ago, in a world that might still have been shaking with the constant eruptions of massive volcanoes, in seas that could have been still warm from the creation of earth.

It all took a very long time to happen. As fast as the sun and the hot earth caused water to evaporate into the atmosphere, it came down again as rain, cooling the earth and slowly filling the oceans. In these early waters, in some first form that we can only

Because living things do not always reproduce exact copies of themselves, the warm seas of our early planet gradually filled with more and more kinds of creatures.

guess at, life finally appeared. Perhaps it disappeared and reappeared millions of times before permanently taking hold. But it was life, and it was able to make copies of itself.

Mostly, these copies were exactly the same, but not always. If they had always been just the same, life never would have changed—it would have continued to reproduce itself endlessly in the same way it had begun. But this was not the case. Occasionally, a change appeared. Usually, this was fatal and the mistake died or could not reproduce itself. But every once in a while the accidental change turned out to be an improvement, and the new form was even more successful than the old one at staying alive in a difficult world.

This new kind of living thing now began to make copies of itself, and again these copies were perfect only most of the time. There were still occasional accidents and mistakes. Each time one of these changes or *mutations* was able to survive and reproduce, there was a different kind of life added to our spinning planet. In many cases, the old form survived along with the new one, so the numbers of kinds of living things kept increasing.

The Oceans Fill with Life

The earth revolved around and around the sun millions and millions of times as these tiny changes took

place. Some of these living things were now able to use the energy from the sun to make food for themselves. These were the first green plants. Other living things took their food from the water about them. These were the first animals. Gradually, the waters filled with primitive life and gradually this life grew more complicated.

Millions more years rolled by. The creatures of the ocean bottom evolved into animals that could swim in all directions through the water. Because of its buoyancy, the water pushed upward under their bodies and relieved these creatures from some of gravity's downward pull. Moving more easily through the water, there was no need for these animals to develop massive legs, and they became sleek and streamlined. And the waters filled with fish.

Life Spills Onto the Land

Eventually, the oceans overflowed with life, and living forms emerged onto the land. But as they moved from the water that had partly buoyed them up and found themselves in the less buoyant air, gravity's pull on them

Stranded on land by retreating tides, some life managed to survive there, and new living things evolved. Two hundred million years later the first bird, Archaeopteryx, was flying.

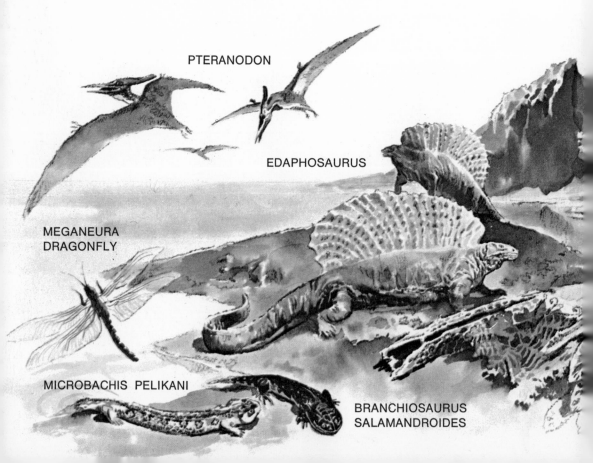

PTERANODON

EDAPHOSAURUS

MEGANEURA
DRAGONFLY

MICROBACHIS PELIKANI

BRANCHIOSAURUS
SALAMANDROIDES

seemed to multiply because it was no longer opposed by buoyancy. You have probably felt the same increased pull on your body when you struggle out of the water onto a beach.

It took a long time for living things to get used to the air. At first, many creatures lived divided lives between the air and water. These in-between creatures, called amphibians, moved awkwardly and slowly over the land. They had fat bodies and small legs, and returned to the water to lay their eggs. After enough time had passed and enough mutations had taken place, there were some creatures that could

ARCHAEOPTERYX

BRONTOSAURUS

move quickly even with the extra tension of gravity. Some animals were eventually able to lay eggs on dry land. These were the first reptiles, and the break with the sea had been established.

The Wild Kingdom became crowded with more and more different types of animals. Insects evolved that had the ability to fly. Dinosaurs, some tiny and some massive, appeared and ruled the earth. As animals became larger, gravity's total effect on them became greater. Larger and larger legs with thicker and thicker bones were necessary. The animals grew larger and larger until *Brontosaurus,* the heaviest creature ever to rumble across the land, had to get relief from some of gravity's pull by spending much of its life half submerged in the more buoyant water. Hippopotamuses do the very same thing today.

Animals Take to the Trees

Animals evolved in ways other than size. Some kinds developed internal controls to keep them warm and active whatever the outside temperature might be. Some others left the ground to live in the trees where food was plentiful and where they were safe from some of the enemies they left behind. Then, perhaps beginning with gentle glides from these same stately trees, another type of animal evolved. During the great age of the dinosaurs, some of the reptiles began actually to fly through the air.

There were two kinds of flying reptiles: the pterodactyl (tair-o-DAK-til) had skin-covered wings, while *Archaeopteryx* (ar-kee-OP-te-ricks) had feathers. The archaeopteryx was not much bigger than a pigeon and probably couldn't fly very well. But its covering of feathers made it the first bird, for, of all the creatures in the Wild Kingdom, only birds have feathers.

Gravity Affects Everything

If we are to understand how birds managed to overcome the pull of gravity in air, we must first understand how their fish ancestors overcame gravity's pull in water. And the important idea to keep in mind as we unravel the story of flight is that gravity affects everything. Not only does it attract the bird and the fish, but the air and water as well.

Obviously, without gravity, the water of our planet would have drifted long ago into space. It's still here because the force of gravity overcomes centripetal force. Gravity attracts every drop of water, every molecule, every atom. It pulls at the surface water and makes it press down on the water beneath it. It pulls at both these waters and makes them press down still harder on the water below them. The farther down you go, the heavier the pile of water becomes. Its weight increases inch by inch. A mile below the surface, gravity is pulling on so much water that a single square-inch column, one mile high, pushes with a force of 2,000 pounds.

This inch-by-inch change in pressure can actually be seen by punching holes at different heights in a tin can and placing it on the edge of a table. When the can is filled with water, the liquid is forced out of the holes at different pressures. The deeper the water, the greater its weight, or pressure. The water squirts out farthest from the lowest hole because the pressure there is greatest. So, the downward pull of gravity on the water is actually pushing it sideways out of the can.

Interestingly, the width of the container has nothing to do with pressure. Water won't squirt any farther from a wider vessel. Only the height of the water determines its pressure.

This force created by gravity is not only exerted sideways, but it pushes up

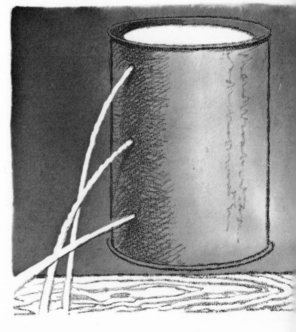

Gravity pulling downward on water forces it out the holes punched in the two tin cans. Water squirts farthest from the bottom hole because it is forced out by greater pressure. An inch upward or downward makes a lot of difference in the amount of pressure water exerts. But notice that the width of the cans does not change these pressures at all.

[25]

Gravity may pull things down, but there are other forces that can push them back up again. These "other" forces explain why the pull of gravity seems to be less on a fish when it is suspended in water. It really is not less. It is just that at the same time that gravity is pulling downward on the fish, the water pushes it upward from underneath.

as well. You can feel this upward push if you try forcing an empty tin can into a basin of water. The water pushes back! Now, if you punch a hole in the bottom of the can and force it into the water, you will be able to see how strong this upward force is, for it will push the water up into the can through the hole.

This buoyancy is what makes you feel lighter when you're sitting in a bathtub full of water than when you have let the water drain out. This upward push of water is what makes you feel lighter when you are swimming or what makes it possible for you to float on your back in the water.

You can actually measure this change in weight caused by water's buoyancy. First weigh a fish out of water; perhaps it weighs two pounds. Then weigh the same fish suspended in water; now the fish will weigh almost nothing. In this case, the water is pushing upward be-

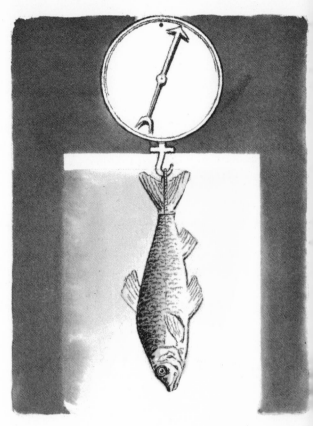

neath the fish and this upward push on the fish is as strong as the downward pull of gravity on it. Since these two forces are in exactly opposite directions and of the same strength, they balance each other. Gravity does not move the fish downward, nor can the buoyancy of the water move the fish upward. In this balanced condition, the fish appears to have no weight at all in water.

There is a similar counterforce in the air, for birds are affected by the same physical laws as fish. The same type of buoyancy found in the water surrounding fish is found in the air surrounding birds and helps push them upward too. Of course, the force of gravity is not as powerful in air as it is in water; a bucket of air does not weigh nearly as much as a bucket of water. But it does weigh something!

Fourteen cubic feet of air near the earth's surface weigh more than a pound. Since the atmosphere around our earth extends at least five hundred miles upward, there is a lot of air piled on top of air, and pressures near the bottom of that pile can be large. A column of air just an inch square but as tall as our entire atmosphere weighs nearly fifteen pounds. A column of air a foot square and as tall as our atmosphere weighs more than a ton.

This great weight presses down on everything—on every square inch of land and water surface, on every living and nonliving thing, even on the pages of this book you're reading right now. What prevents "The Miracle of Flight" from being pushed out of your hands and slammed against the floor is an almost equal upward push from the air beneath it! The weight of air creates forces in all directions in the same way that the weight of water creates forces in all directions. These forces push downward, sideward, and upward! And they push with about equal strength all about the book. The sideward forces balance one another, so the book doesn't move sideways. The upward and downward forces balance one another too. Only gravity's tug on the book is not counterbalanced, so it tugs gently at it, urging it toward the floor.

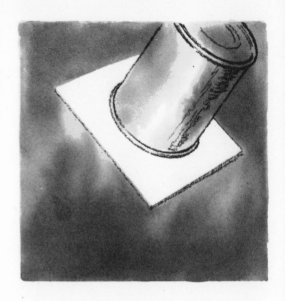

Air pressure pushing against the cardboard exerts enough force to keep the water in an upside-down can from doing what it otherwise would do—fall earthward.

The Weight of Air Pushes Things Up

We sometimes have trouble imagining what an upward push really is

Gravity pulls on air, compressing it near the earth's surface. Air pressure beneath a bird's wings supports it in exactly the same way water pressure buoys up a fish.

—especially when the material doing the pushing is invisible. One way to see air push upward is to fill a tin can with water, then cover it with a piece of cardboard. Holding the cardboard tightly against the top of the can, turn the whole thing upside down. You can now safely let go of the cardboard and the water will stay up in the can, held there by the upward push of air. The upward force of nearly fifteen pounds per square inch on the cardboard is greater than gravity's downward pull on the water.

The "trick" here is that only the upward push of air is being allowed to act on the water. In the case of the book, the downward push of air on the book was balanced by the upward push. In this case, however, the downward push that would normally be acting on the water is prevented from touching it by the metal bottom of the can. Without this balancing force, the upward force is great enough to hold the water up in the can. But just punch a hole in the bottom of the can and air will immediately rush in through it. Now the air pressures are balanced again. In this more usual situation, the water and cardboard will be pulled toward earth.

The point of all this is that, when you eliminate or reduce the downward push of air, the remaining upward push can exert great lifting force. Another way you can see this force operate is to drop a small, burning piece of paper into an empty milk bottle, cap the bottle quickly with a hard-boiled egg (shell removed, of course), and turn it upside down. The egg will squeeze itself upward through the narrow neck and pop into the bottle!

Here, the pressures are unbalanced by the burning paper. The heat causes the air in the bottle to expand, which, in turn, causes some of the air to escape. This leaves less air inside to press down against the egg. As the air inside cools and contracts, the pressure of the air outside the bottle is great enough to push the egg up. (To get the egg out again without breaking it, turn the bottle upside down, with the egg resting in the neck of the bottle and acting as an inside stopper. Carefully blow air into the bottle around the egg.

When pressure has built up sufficiently inside the bottle, it will slowly force the egg back out through the narrow bottle neck.)

Birds and planes aren't eggs, but their flight is dependent on the same forces that moved the egg up into the bottle. If the birds and planes could somehow reduce the downward push of air above them, the upward push of air beneath them might make it possible to fly.

But the pressure above the egg is reduced in a closed container. It's not difficult to reduce pressure in a closed bottle. The water stays up in the tin can because it's not too dif-ficult to unbalance pressures in a closed tin can. But birds and planes don't operate in containers. However, reducing the pressure above birds' wings turns out to be almost as simple as the two experiments we have just described.

It happens in a slightly different way, but the results are identical. Pressures are reduced above their wings in such a way that the normal upward push of air beneath these wings counteracts the downward pull of gravity. Man tried for thousands of years to discover this design for flight. Now that he finally knows it, he too can soar away from earth, with the birds.

An egg will be drawn upward into a milk bottle when air pressure is reduced above the egg. Birds reduce the air pressure above their wings and are drawn upward in a similar way.

Chapter 3

DESIGN FOR FLIGHT

THERE are two ways for a bird to move upward. If the pressure above its wings can be reduced, the bird will literally be sucked up into the air, as if a giant vacuum cleaner were operating above it. Another way is for the pressure below its wings to be increased. This blows the bird upward, as a hat is blown by the wind or a kite is pushed upward.

Actually, both these forces operate on birds. Birds are both pushed from below and pulled from above at the same time. These are called *aerodynamic forces*. But before any of these forces can begin operating on a bird,

movement is necessary. Either the bird must be moving through the air, or the air must be moving past the bird.

It doesn't matter which moves past what. All that is necessary is that one be moving past the other. After all, to get a kite away from the ground, you usually have to run with it, pulling it through the quieter air near the ground until it reaches the faster-moving air higher up. In addition, it is not necessary for the air to be moving upward against the bird in order for the bird to be forced upward, just as it is not necessary for the air to be

moving upward against the kite to move it upward.

You can feel how horizontally moving air pushes upward if you hold your arm out the window of a moving car. With your palm facing forward, moving air pushes straight against it. But as you slowly change the angle of your hand by turning the palm partially toward the ground, the air begins pushing up as well as back. This is how a kite is angled against the wind. The moving air pushes the kite up and back just as it does your hand. The string prevents the kite from moving back, so the force of the moving air can only push it upward.

What happens when the kite or your hand or any flat object is angled this way? The force of horizontally moving air is being used to overcome the downward pull of gravity. The faster the air strikes any of these objects, the greater will be its upward push.

The same thing happens in water. If a water skier is moving fast enough, the force of the water pushing up against his skis is great enough to overcome the pull of gravity, and he remains on top of the water. But as the speed of the skis against the water is reduced, the upward force of the water against the skis is reduced too. If the motion of the skis stops completely, there is no longer any moving stream of water to form any upward push. The only force left supporting the skier is the normal buoyancy of the water itself. Since this is not great enough to counterbalance gravity, the skier will get dunked.

If this same skier attaches a very large kite to his arms and the boat pulls him quickly enough against the air, he can use the moving air to overcome gravity's pull. If the air is moving fast enough against the surface of his kite, he will rise into the air just as any other kite, as your hand against the rushing air outside the car, as the skis against the oncoming water. Moving air pushes kites away from the earth and it helps push birds and jet planes skyward too.

So far there is nothing surprising about any of this. We accept the idea that moving air pushes things, that it can support kites, turn windmills, move sailboats, blow hats from our heads, and overturn giant trees. If we hold a piece of paper by one of its edges and blow against it, we'd be very surprised if the air didn't push the paper away from us.

But what happens when we blow *over* the paper instead of against it? It goes up again! Now this is somewhat unusual. A moving stream of air under it or over it moves the paper in the same upward direction. If we substitute a wing for the paper, the same thing happens. A moving stream of air under it or over it exerts push in an upward direction.

The explanation for this not-quite-what-you-might-expect movement involves a principle discovered more than two hundred years ago by a man who certainly never thought of applying it to flying! He was Daniel Bernoulli, one of a family of Swiss scientists and mathematicians. In 1738 he published a paper about fluids and the pressures they exert when they move. Bernoulli was interested in liquids, but many of the things he discovered are true about gases as well. For liquids and gases are both fluids.

Bernoulli's Principle

At some time or another, you probably stuck your hand into the water coming out of a garden hose. If the nozzle was fully opened and the water was rushing out, you could feel the considerable force exerted by that moving water. But what you couldn't really feel was the pressure the water was exerting against the inside of the garden hose.

If you had a nozzle at the end of the hose that you could close all the way, the pressure of the water would be bottled up inside the hose and would push against it. If the nozzle were opened again, this pressure against the inside of the hose would drop. Bernoulli's discovery was that these pres-

Water moving slowly through hose (top) exerts enough pressure against inside of hose to operate sprinkler vigorously.
When valve is opened fully, the water moves more quickly through hose (center), but exerts less pressure and operates sprinkler weakly.
The same thing happens with gas (bottom). To get through narrow part of the tube, gas speeds up, exerts less pressure, produces smaller flame.

sures are related to the speed of the moving fluid. The faster the fluid is moving forward, the less pressure it exerts; the slower it moves, the greater this pressure will be.

Bernoulli's Principle operates whether the fluid is in a container or is flowing freely. And it operates whether the fluid is a liquid such as water or a gas such as air. Bernoulli's discovery explains why the wings of birds and planes are sucked upward, and why a piece of paper goes up when you blow over it.

Take the paper first. When the air in a room is still, it is exerting pressure equally on its two sides. The push from the air on one side of the paper is the same as the push on the other side. Since these pushes balance one another, the paper doesn't move.

But when you begin blowing over the top of the paper, you cause the air to move faster there, and Bernoulli's Principle goes into operation. The faster the air moves above the paper, the less pressure it exerts there. Since nothing has happened to change the pressure below the paper, it remains the same. The result is that the pressures are no longer balanced. The pressure on the bottom of the paper is greater than the pressure above it, and this greater pressure pushes the paper up.

In this simple principle is the key to the miracle of flight. For it is this same pressure that pushes against the underside of the wings of birds and planes and lifts them into the air.

Here is how Bernoulli's Principle works on wings. If you cut through the

Bernoulli's Principle explains how a moving stream of air above a piece of paper reduces the pressure there and moves the paper upward. It is this same kind of air movement above birds' wings that lifts them into the air.

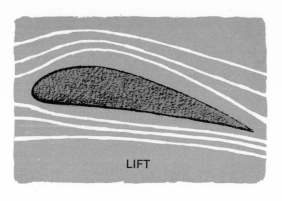

LIFT

Reduced pressure above airfoil creates lift.

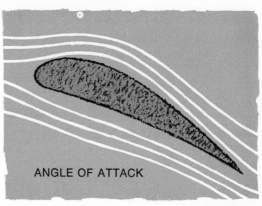

ANGLE OF ATTACK

Increasing angle of attack increases lift.

inner section of any wing, bird or plane, you'll find it has a distinctive profile that has come to be known as an *airfoil*. As the wing moves through the air, air flows smoothly above and below its streamlined shape. But because the curve on the upper surface of the wing is larger than the one beneath it, air passing over the wing is forced to travel a greater distance to get past the wing than air passing beneath it. Therefore, to arrive at the trailing edge of the wing at the same time, the upper airstream is forced to speed up. As it does, Bernoulli's Principle goes into effect.

Because air is moving faster above the wing, the pressure it exerts there is reduced. The pressure beneath the wing is now relatively greater. When the pressure above the wing is reduced enough, the unchanged pressure below the wing will actually be able to push the wing upward. This is called *lift*.

Both birds and planes are lifted into the air by this upward push. The greater their weight, the more lift they need. The amount of lift that a wing can produce is determined by several different things. One of these is the size of the wing. Since the pressure that creates lift is exerted against the entire undersurface of the wing, the larger the wing the larger this upward push or lift can be. In general, if the size of the wing is doubled, lift is doubled.

Another way that lift can be increased is to change the angle of the wing. When the leading edge of the wing is tilted upward, the distance air must travel above the wing increases. This speeds it up still more—and so lift is increased still more. This angle at which a wing approaches the oncoming air is called the *angle of attack*. A jet plane changes this by lowering flaps along the trailing edge of the wings. A bird does it by changing the

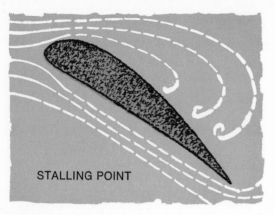

STALLING POINT

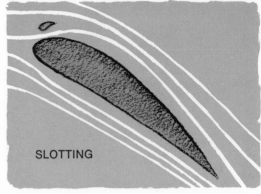

SLOTTING

If upper airstream breaks away, lift vanishes.   *Slot restores lift by speeding up airstream.*

angle of its entire wing. Either method increases lift enormously. Twice the angle of attack gives about twice the lift. Increasing the angle still more gives even more lift up to a point— then suddenly all lift disappears! When this happens the bird or plane has *stalled* and immediately begins falling toward earth.

The force that keeps the bird or plane from falling is the lift created by the reduced pressure on top of the wing. Another way to describe this reduced pressure area above the wing is to call it a partial vacuum. But whatever you call it, what causes it suddenly to disappear?

At first, as the angle of attack increases, the vacuum, or lift, increases. This same vacuum holds the airstream close to the wing. But as the angle of attack continues to increase, it becomes more and more difficult for the airstream to hang on to the top of the wing. At a certain point, the angle be-

comes too steep. Even though the vacuum is strong, it is not strong enough to hold the airstream in place, and the airstream breaks away from the wing. As soon as it does, all lift disappears. The bird or plane has reached the stalling point.

Slotting and Lift

There is a way, however, to restore this lost lift without reducing the angle of attack. If the air passing above the wing can somehow be made to move faster still, the vacuum between it and the wing will be increased. If this vacuum can be strengthened enough to pull the airstream back down along the wing again, the flying machine is back in business.

The technique used to make the upper airstream move faster is to force it through a small slot just ahead of the upper surface of the wing. To squeeze all of itself through this small opening requires the airstream to speed up. This increases the vacuum between it and the wing, pulling the airstream back down where it belongs, against the wing. And so, lift can be restored by slots in the wing.

These slots are formed in a number of different ways. On birds, the easiest to see are the adjustable *alulas* in front of each wing. Formed by a few feathers attached to a movable finger bone, they are very much like our thumbs. You can somewhat duplicate the effect of the alula with your hand outside the window of a car again. At about fifty miles an hour, hold your hand at the correct angle of attack and move the thumb up and down to open and close the slot. You should be able to feel a strong increase and decrease in the amount of lift your arm gets as you operate the slot.

Birds have other kinds of slots. They can manipulate the feathers at their wing tips to provide slots there if needed. They can also lift the feathers on the leading edge of the wing to form slots right through the wing. Any of these techniques that increase the speed of air as it moves over the upper surface of a wing increases lift. Obviously then, if the entire wing can be made to move faster through the air, lift will also be increased.

Speed, therefore, is the most important element in lift. Of all the things that affect the amount of lift, increases in the forward speed of the wing through the air produce the most dramatic changes. If the speed is doubled, the lift increases nearly four times; if it is tripled, the lift increases nine times.

Just how much lift is needed varies with the weight of the bird. The heavier the animal, the more lift it needs. It also depends on whether the bird is moving up or down or is in level flight. For example, to move upward, lift must be greater than the downward pull of gravity on the bird's body. For level flight, it need only be equal to the pull of gravity. As long as these two forces, lift and gravity, are balanced, the bird will remain at the same altitude. To move downward, lift must be less than gravity.

Some birds have large wings that produce enormous lift at very low speeds. Other birds with smaller wings must be moving faster before they can be airborne. Just what minimum speed is needed to create enough lift for flight depends, then, on the design of the bird. Since, for most birds, no lift is created unless the bird is moving forward through the air, the next question that must be answered is: What creates the forward motion of birds?

Chapter 4

POWERED FLIGHT

JET airplanes move forward through the air by pushing hot gases from the rear of their engines. Propeller-driven planes move forward by pushing air backward with the spinning blades of their propellers. Birds get their forward thrust from the flapping of their wings.

But the more you think about flapping wings, the more difficult it is to see how they propel a bird forward. What has an up and down motion got to do with pushing a bird forward? It seems reasonable enough that the downward push of the rigid wings against the air might move a bird upward. But if that happens, what about the other half of the wingbeat? Why wouldn't the upward movement of the wings push the bird right back down again? It should be clear that we need to know more about these remarkable structures before we can further understand the miracle of flight.

Wing Construction

If we compare the bone structure of bird wings with our own arms, we see a great similarity in design. In fact, one of the most fascinating things about the Wild Kingdom is the similarity that is often found among all the living things. In birds and men, the basic bone structure of the wing and arm is very much the same except in the area of the hand.

This isn't too strange since arms and wings are both modifications of the front legs of far distant ancestors, but each evolved very differently. In man, the hand has become more complicated. It has developed into a structure that can make and use the most complicated tools. In man, fingers have become so skillful they can hold a pencil or push the keys of a typewriter to record thoughts on paper. But the evolution of the bird's wing from the foreleg has been different. Its "hand" has become less rather than more complicated. Many of the bones are fused together and many others have completely disappeared. Men have twenty-nine bones in each arm; some birds have only eleven. Those bones that remain in the bird's hand are proportionately much longer and narrower than ours.

With fewer bones, there are fewer joints in a bird's wing, so fewer movements are possible. The hand section of a wing is much less flexible than our hand, but this rigidity makes it stronger. And great strength is needed, for the hand section of the wing creates the power that drives the bird forward through the air. This outer section of the wing is where the greatest strains of flight occur.

To help withstand these strains, the joints that remain in the wing are designed in a special way. A bird's "wrist," for example, does not rotate like ours. The bird does not have to use muscles to keep its hand angled properly against the air. Instead, the bones are joined together so that the hand section is automatically in proper alignment with the rest of the wing. The bird's "elbow" is designed so that it cannot bend in the direction that receives the greatest stress during flight. Again, this eliminates the need for special muscles to hold the wing stiff.

The "shoulder joint," too, is shaped so that it automatically holds the inner sections of the wing at the proper angle of attack for the most effective lift. This section of the wing between the shoulder and the wrist moves very little during flight. It has the most pronounced airfoil shape and corresponds most to the wing of an airplane. It provides the properly curved surfaces that form lift as the bird moves forward.

The construction of the joints, however, does allow certain movements. When the bird is not in flight, the three sections of the wing can be folded back into a tight Z against the side of the body, somewhat like the retractable landing gear of planes, except that these sections of the wing are the bird's

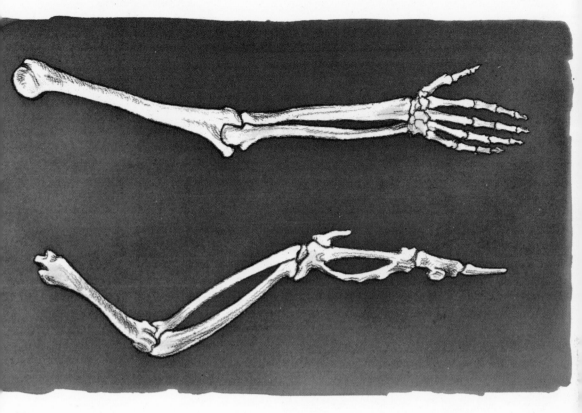

The bone structure of a man's arm and a bird's wing are very much alike—except for the "hand" section. Some of the bird's finger bones have fused together and have grown longer.

retractable flying gear. And when they are extended, they are both wings and propellers. For sticking out from the hand, or end section, of a bird's wings are a series of remarkable feathers that correspond to the propellers of a piston-driven plane. These special feathers create the forward thrust.

Feathers

Feathers have not always been so closely associated with flight, but feath-ers are the characteristic that distin-guishes present-day birds from all the other creatures in the Wild Kingdom. It's not the ability to fly that defines a bird, for some birds cannot fly and some animals like bats, which aren't birds, can fly. But no animal except a bird has feathers.

Today, bird flight can't be under-stood without studying feathers, even though the original development of feathers probably had nothing to do with flying. More likely, the first feath-ers were a protection for their owners

[47]

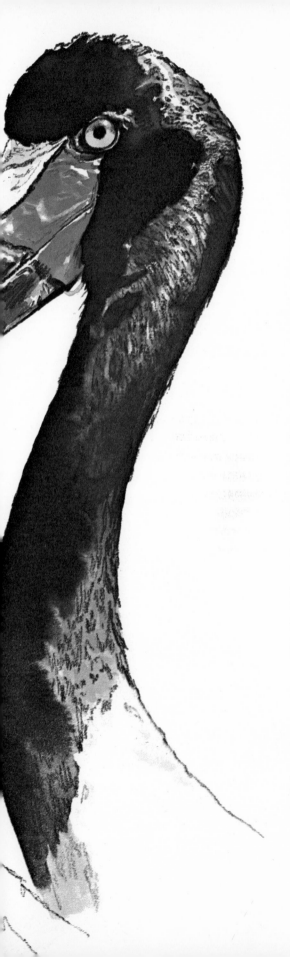

against the cold, just as the development of hair gave protection to mammals.

Feathers and fur are good insulation; they prevent an animal's body heat from being lost to the outside air. This insulation made it possible for animals to develop with more constant internal temperatures. In fact, feathers and fur are such excellent insulation that birds and mammals are able to live in even the coldest parts of our earth. Of all the creatures in the Wild Kingdom, only feathered and furred animals ever became warm-blooded.

We usually think of all feathers as the same, but there are two distinct types: *down* and *vaned* feathers. The down feathers are the fluffy ones that are used to stuff pillows and quilts. The vaned are the kind used many years ago to make quill pens, and they form the sleek outer covering of the bird. The disheveled down feathers lie beneath them and are closest to the bird's body. The silken, hairlike *barbs* of these down feathers tumble this way and that, forming millions of tiny air spaces among their tangle. This is why they are such good insulation. Heat does not move easily through air, so these many pockets of air effectively prevent the bird's body heat from escaping.

Birds are among the most brilliantly colored animals on earth. Though feathers are sometimes different in outward appearance, their basic design is very much alike.

The degree of insulation these feathers can provide is adjustable. Muscles in the skin can fluff the feathers to create still more pockets of air, or the feathers can be pulled more tightly against the skin to squeeze out some of these insulating air pockets. During winter, when maximum insulation is needed, the number of these insulating feathers may actually increase.

Today, feathers do more than just insulate. During the millions and millions of years that followed the appearance of the first insulating feathers, some of them became modified to perform additional duties.

Certain feathers became extremely useful for flight. The descendants of those early reptiles whose scales turned into feathers are still around today. They are the birds that live in every part of the Wild Kingdom. The pterodactyls, on the other hand, were those other prehistoric flying reptiles that for some reason did not develop feathers. They long ago disappeared.

The special feathers that became modified to aid flight are very different from the fluffy down feathers. These are the sleek vaned feathers and there are two kinds: *contour* and *flight*. The contours are the outside feathers of a bird and further help to smooth and streamline the body shape. When the bird coats these feathers with special waterproofing oil produced in a gland near its tail, they act as a raincoat. The flight feathers are on the wings and tail and are the ones that make flight possible.

What makes the flight and contour feathers smooth and hard instead of frazzled like down feathers is an ingenious system of hooks. These hooks tie the hundreds of individual barbs into two neat, flat sheets, or *vanes*, one on either side of the shaft. Down feathers don't have these hooks.

When you first look at one of the vanes of a feather, it appears solid. A closer examination, however, reveals that the barbs are all lined up one next to the other. They can easily be separated, and then with a gentle stroke of the finger can just as easily be hooked back together again. These barbs can be hooked and unhooked repeatedly without damage, much like

The barbs of down feathers have no special hooks to attach to one another, and so they sprawl about in all directions.

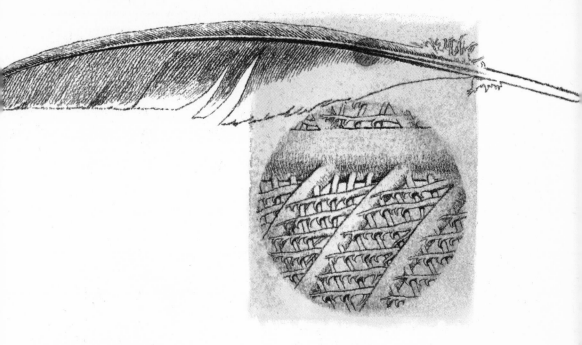

Jutting out from each side of the heavy central shaft or quill of a vaned feather are hundreds of hairlike barbs.
The enlargement shows microscopic hooks that lock the individual barbs together into two strong sheets called vanes.

a zipper can be hooked and unhooked.

Here's how it works: each barb has two rows of smaller projections called *barbules* growing out from either side of it. The barbules of one barb overlap those of the barbs next to it. But the barbules of these overlapping rows are not exactly the same; there's an important difference in their shape. One row will have small projections that curl down; the row it overlaps will have projections that curl up. These neatly hook into one another and lock the barbules of one barb to those of its neighbor, holding all of them together in a strong, flat sheet. The hooks can slide sideways a considerable distance before unlocking, so the vane can bend quite far before it comes apart. Even when it does become parted by accident or ordinary wear and tear, it will either automatically rehook itself or the bird can do this when it *preens,* by drawing the parted feather through its bill.

In a world where so few things are interchangeable, it's remarkable to find the zipper system of feathers just about the same in all birds. Fishermen make elaborate casting flies by gently stroking together the feathers of completely unrelated birds, and these feathers will hook to one another

Primary feathers (green) drive the bird forward, secondaries (yellow) form the wing's lifting surface, tertiaries (gray) close the gap near the body, and alulas (blue) form the movable slot.

as easily as if they had all come from the same bird.

Feathers grow from the bird's skin, and are like our hair and nails in that they're alive only as long as they are being formed. When feathers reach full size, they harden and the supply of food to them stops. Full-grown feathers are composed of dead skin cells, and though very strong and durable, they do wear out and they do get damaged. So, periodically, old feath-

But some species of birds have two annual molts, some even more than that. If a feather becomes worn and drops out, cells responsible for feather growth are stimulated to provide the bird with a prompt replacement. Even the larger feathers can be regrown in just a few weeks.

During the regular molting period, most birds do not suddenly lose all their feathers. Worn ones are dropped just a few at a time, for if a bird lost too many at once it might not be able to survive a sudden temperature drop. In addition, the feathers that are essential to flight usually fall out in pairs during molting, one from each side of the bird, and in a very definite sequence depending upon the kind of bird. Only when the first pair has almost been replaced, does a second pair drop out. This cautious replacement prevents the bird from being grounded.

Ducks, swans, and geese are exceptions to this; they do lose all their flight feathers at once. Being water animals, however, they're still able to get food. Generally, during this vulnerable period when they can't fly from danger, they try to avoid it by hiding. Only when the flight feathers have grown out again can these birds take to the air.

Considering the great number of feathers that cover a bird, only a very few of them are absolutely essential for flight. These feathers are all very large, vaned ones that grow on the wings and tail of a bird and extend beyond its body.

Most flying birds have ten flight

ers are pushed out by new ones that grow under them.

This orderly and automatic replacement of feathers is called *molting*. In most birds it happens once each year, usually just after the breeding season.

feathers, called *primaries,* on the end section of each wing. *Secondaries* are attached to the middle section of the wing between wrist and elbow and form most of the wing's lifting surface. The longer the bird's wing, the more secondaries it will have. A few vaned feathers, called *tertiaries* (TER-shuh-reez), grow on the upper arm sections between elbow and shoulder and help close the gap between the wing and the bird's body. A few more small, vaned flight feathers are attached to the "thumb" of the end, or hand section, to form the *alula,* the tiny wing just ahead of the main wing. Finally, ten or twelve vaned flight feathers form the bird's tail.

At first, one vaned flight feather looks like any other. But if you compare one of the tail feathers with one of the primary or secondary feathers from the wing, you will notice a very important difference. The shaft of a wing feather does not run down the center of the feather, but is considerably off-center. The vanes on either side of the shaft, therefore, are not of equal size. It is this extremely simple change in design that makes it possible for the wing feathers to push a bird forward.

Forward Thrust

To understand how these particular feathers push a bird forward, it is necessary first to understand that all forward motion is the result of pushing backward.

You walk forward by pushing backward against the ground with your feet. If you sit in a rowboat and push against the pier, the boat will move in the opposite direction. The boat will continue to move forward if you keep pushing backward against the water with oars. Bicycles and automobiles move forward because their wheels push backward against the ground. A bird moves forward by pushing backward with its own special kind of moving propellers—the primary flight feathers at the ends of its wings.

At first, it is difficult to see how the bird's propellers work because we are used to thinking of propellers as spinning blades. Obviously, bird's propellers can't spin around. Only man-made devices are able to make complete revolutions. The nerves and blood vessels of the Wild Kingdom's creatures would be destroyed if they were twisted that far. In spite of this, the primary feathers at the end of the wing do exactly the same thing as the propeller of an airplane or the blade of a fan: they push backward against the air. But they do it half a revolution at a time.

On the downstroke, these large wing feathers push backward against the air. This is the same as the first half of a revolution of a plane's propeller. Then the feathers twist over in such a way that they push air backward on the upstroke too! This is the second half of the revolution. Back and forth the feathers twist as the wing moves up and down. And the thing that makes them turn over is the peculiar off-center position of their shafts. Flight feathers in the tail, with shafts down the center, do not twist.

If you have two of these different kinds of flight feathers, you can actually see how the design makes some of them turn. For example, if you hold one of the vaned tail feathers by its shaft and move it quickly up and down through the air, nothing unexpected happens. That is because the shaft of these feathers runs right down the center, dividing the web into two vanes of equal size. But if you do the same thing with one of the vaned primary or secondary feathers, it will twist first one way and then the other as you move it first up and then down through the air. Since this twisting works in your hand, it obviously is not controlled by any muscles of the bird. The twisting of these feathers is completely automatic—and is caused by the unequal size of their vanes.

Because the vanes on either side of the shaft are of different sizes, air acts differently on them as they move up and down through it. The larger vane bumps into more air than the smaller one as the feather moves. During the upstroke, more air particles strike the top of the larger vane than the smaller one, so this part of the feather is pushed down. During the downstroke, air pressure is again greater on the larger vane, but this time the pressure pushes it up, twisting the feather in the opposite direction. As the wing moves up and down through the air, all the flight feathers

with these off-center shafts twist back and forth.

Only the secondary and primary feathers do this twisting. The secondaries are the feathers that make up the inside section of the wing and are quite close to one another. When they twist back and forth it's like the slats of a Venetian blind opening and closing. During the upstroke, they twist and *open* the wing so that air can pass easily between them. In this position they offer little resistance to the air and so the upstroke is very fast. But as soon as the bird begins its downstroke, the secondaries automatically twist the other way and snap tightly against one another, again like a Venetian blind. They *close* the wing and form an almost airtight surface that can push downward and backward with great force against the air.

The primaries at the ends of the wing are even more important in propelling the bird forward, for they move the greatest distance. (If you swing your arms up and down in imitation of the movement of a bird's wing, your hands will move much greater distances than will your elbows.) The primaries are not too close together, and they do not interfere with one another as they twist back and forth. They are stiffer than any of the other feathers, and their barbs are thick near the base, which gives them an airfoil shape. Like the secondaries, they have different-sized vanes and twist back and forth as the wing moves up and down. It is these ten feathers at the end of each wing that give the bird its main forward thrust.

A

B

As the downstroke begins, the flight feathers are twisted automatically into their proper power position.

Angled like the blades of a propeller, the flight feathers at the ends of the wings bite through the air.

The Strokes

At the beginning of the downstroke (Position A, above), the wider vanes at the back of each primary feather are twisted up. This presents each of these propeller feathers at just the proper angle of attack to the air. As the powerful breast muscles of the bird pull the entire wing downward, each primary feather bites through the air and pushes backward against it (Position B). These strong, stiff feathers create forward thrust for the bird in exactly the same way as the propeller blades of a piston plane.

As the wings move downward, the underside of each primary feather continues to push backward against the air. At the same time, because of its airfoil shape, a partial vacuum forms on the upper surface. Since at this point of the stroke the upper surface of each primary is facing forward, it

C

D

Pushing backward against the air, the primaries are forced forward, pulling the wings along with them.

At the end of the downstroke, the wings may be in front of a bird's head, especially during strenuous takeoffs.

is sucked forward by the vacuum ahead of it. During the downstroke, then, all these propeller feathers are both pushing against the air behind them and being pulled from in front, forcing them forward (Position C).

The secondaries that form the center sections of the wings are also snapped into their power position at the beginning of the downstroke. Now, as the tightly closed wings move downward, their entire undersurfaces push downward and backward against the air,

helping to move the bird both forward and upward. There is enormous resistance from the air to the downward movement of these great, flat surfaces, and it slows the wings' movement. Tremendous power is required to overcome this resistance. The muscles that pull the wings down in their closed power position are often ten times as large as those needed to pull them back up again. In most small birds, the powerful downstroke supplies all the forward thrust needed.

E

F

The moment the upstroke begins, the flight feathers automatically twist 90 degrees like Venetian blinds.

Air passes easily through the opened flight feathers as the wings sweep quickly upward, doing little propelling.

During the downstroke, the bird's muscles pull only straight downward on the two wings. But as the individual feather propellers move downward, they are forced forward at the same time by the pressures that have built up on either side of them. And since they are attached to the wings they drag the wings forward with them. At the bottom of the downstroke, therefore, the wings may be far ahead of the body (Position D, page 57). A split second later, of course, the body will catch up. This pulling ahead of the wings is especially noticeable at takeoff when the bird's body resists moving. In steady flight, however, the body does not lag quite as far behind the wings.

Now the large muscles relax and the smaller breast muscles start to pull the wings upward (Position E). Just as soon as the wings begin to move in this opposite direction, the air twists the flight feathers and the wings open like Venetian blinds (Position F). The open passages between the feathers let

G

H

During the upstroke, wings appear to move backward. Actually, the bird's body is catching up with its wings.

At the end of the upstroke, the wings are far back. In another instant, the cycle begins again as the flight feathers close.

air slip through, so the air offers little resistance to the wings' movement; the upstroke is fast and easy. Some birds reduce still more the amount of air resistance they will meet by drawing their wings close to the body on the upstroke.

For most birds, this upstroke is just a method for returning the wings to a starting position for the power stroke. But some of the larger birds have primaries angled in such a way that they can do a little propelling on the

upstroke, too. They push some air backward and so create a small amount of forward thrust. As the upstroke continues, the wings appear to be moving backward at the same time (Position G). This is mostly an illusion. The wings aren't moving backward, rather the body is moving forward. It is catching up with the wings that got ahead of it during the downstroke.

At the top of the upstroke, the wings are once again in the starting position to begin the downstroke, with one important difference: the flight feathers are still in their "open" position. But once the major breast muscles take over again and begin to move the wings downward, the flight feathers will automatically twist and close the wings for the start of a new power stroke (Position H, page 59).

Over and over, the cycle repeats itself. The aerodynamic design of the propeller feathers pulls the wings forward as the bird moves them downward, and then the body pulls itself up alongside the wings on the upstroke. All the time the outer sections of the wings are going through these complicated contortions to push the bird forward, the inner sections of the wings are forming the broad surfaces that supply the lift the bird needs to stay in the air.

This description of a single wing-beat has taken some time to read; in actual flight it is over in an instant. No wonder it took men so many years to unravel even a few of the remarkable facts about how birds fly. And if it had not been for the invention of the high-speed camera, we probably still would not know much more than ancient man knew about the miracle of flight.

Chapter 5

GLIDING FLIGHT

AS REMARKABLE as powered flight is, flight without power is even more intriguing. Good sense tells us there must be some form of energy expended to oppose gravity, yet there are birds that can glide and soar for hours without moving their wings. The Laysan and black-footed albatrosses of Midway Island can do this. Eagles will glide for miles over their "territory" with wings quietly outstretched. Huge vultures can soar majestically through the air, seemingly unaffected by the pull of gravity. If the wings do not move, the power for flight cannot be coming from them. And if it is not coming from the wings, where does it come from? Gliding takes a little explanation to understand fully.

If you drop a basketball, gravity attracts it downward in an almost straight path toward the ground. But if you let go of that same ball when it is resting on the side of a hill, gravity pulls it down a somewhat different path. The ball rolls down the hill—

which means that not only is it going downward, but it is going sideward, too!

Almost the same thing happens to a gliding bird. When it opens its wings, it can rest them on an invisible hill of air. The air interferes with gravity's pull. Instead of being yanked straight down, the bird glides more slowly down its hill of air. Just as it pulled the basketball in two directions, gravity makes the bird move forward as well as downward.

This forward motion creates lift above the wings, and slows the bird's descent toward earth even more. It does not completely stop it, however, for even the most efficiently designed bird cannot glide against the force of gravity forever. Eventually, gravity must win out and bring the bird back to earth. Yet we see many birds apparently breaking this simple law of physics and common sense. These birds float gently in the air without flapping their wings, and are even able to glide upward. If the additional force needed to overcome the pull of gravity is not coming from the movement of the wings, where is it coming from? What is the secret of some birds' ability to stay in the air for hours without moving their wings?

Thermals

Actually, these birds are taking advantage of upward movements of air called *thermals*. Instead of resting their outstretched wings on quiet hills of air, these birds are resting them on piles of air that are in fact moving upward. We usually cannot feel these updrafts near the ground, and only occasionally are we able to see any indication of them. For example, under the burning desert sun, distant objects seem to quiver. Or lying on your stomach at the beach you can sometimes see wiggling lines above the hot sand. Or looking over the heated hood of an automobile, distant objects seem to tremble. All these effects are a result of your looking through waving currents of warm air rising from these surfaces. You cannot see the air itself, but you can see the way it distorts objects behind it.

At best, you may be able to observe this effect for a few feet. But long after it is completely invisible to you, the air continues moving upward. Many different kinds of gliding birds are able to find these rising currents of air and use the extra upward push they give. Added to the normal aerodynamic lift of the bird's wings, it may be enough finally to overcome the pull of gravity —and no additional power from flapping is necessary. These birds are gliding downward in a constantly rising current of air, so they can stay aloft for hours without moving their wings.

Recent studies have shown that

Hot air often boils up from the ground to form giant, invisible, doughnut-shaped bubbles. Gliding birds find these rising thermals and use them for support, circling about on them for easy, effortless rides upward.

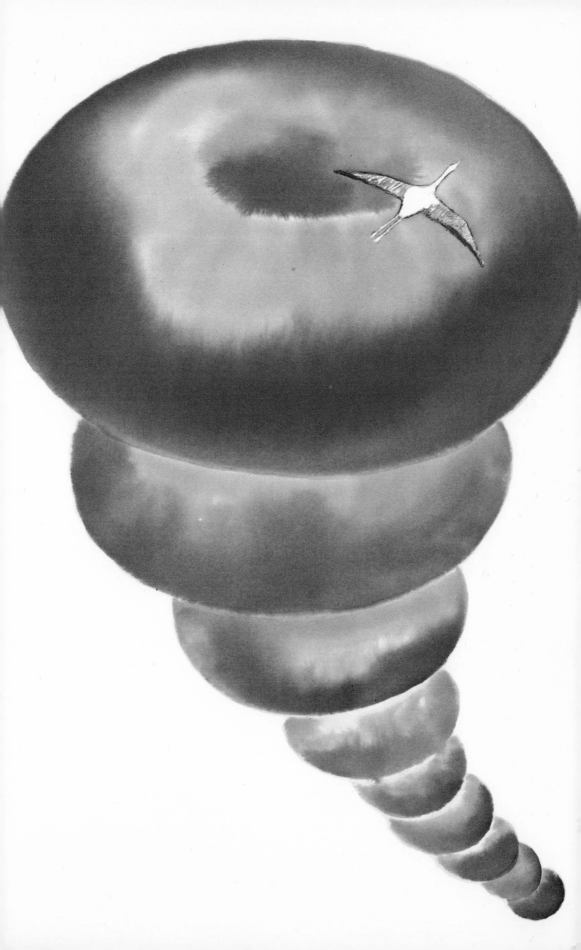

heated air does not always rise evenly from the surface of the earth. Sometimes it moves upward like the bubbles in a pot of gently boiling water. These bubbles are doughnut-shaped, with the air moving up through the center and then tumbling down around the outside of the ring. Some soaring birds find the rising air inside these rings and let it help push them upward. They circle around and around inside the ring, and as the whole ring gradually rises, the circling birds are carried upward too.

Eventually, however, even the most extensive thermal thins out to a point where it can no longer push a bird upward. When this happens, the bird takes off in a straight glide, gently falling toward earth until it catches a ride on another and stronger rising bubble of air.

Where thermals exist, riding them is a great energy-saving scheme. Unfortunately, thermals do not exist everywhere, and they do not operate at all hours of the day. Unless the sun has been out long enough to have heated the ground sufficiently, there aren't any thermals at all. It is quite common to see some of the big gliding birds waiting around on the ground until the thermals finally do begin to rise about nine or ten o'clock in the morning.

There are other kinds of updrafts besides thermals. One is called an *obstruction current*. This forms when moving air runs into a hill or cliff or mountain or even a building—and is forced to rise over it. Some birds may use these rising currents of air to conserve energy. Sea birds, however, like the albatross, take advantage of a still different kind of air movement. They use the relatively steady power of ocean breezes like the trade winds to rise and glide downward in almost endless cycles. This is called *dynamic soaring*.

But even the birds that make the best use of these different energy-saving air currents must in the end use powered flight. They need it when these currents are not available and they need it to get up to these currents when they are available. So while all birds can do some gliding and some birds glide a great deal of the time, all flying birds must in the end be able to supply themselves with all the energy they need for flight. The flapping of their wings is the critical source of that power and control—and it is absolutely essential at the beginning and end of each flight.

Chapter 6

TAKEOFF AND LANDING

THE most dangerous moments in the flight of any bird or plane are during takeoff and landing. Because the amount of aerodynamic lift is related to the forward speed of the plane or bird, lift is weakest at takeoff before full flight speed is reached, and again at landing as speed is being reduced.

But things other than speed affect the amount of lift created, so there are ways available to make up for this temporary loss of lift. The size of the wing helps determine how much lift is formed, so the ailerons and flaps of modern jetliners slide out of the back of the wings to make them larger during takeoff and landing. This gives the

planes extra lift at low speeds. The angle at which the wing approaches the air also affects the amount of lift, so all planes have flaps they can lower to increase this angle and so increase lift. Planes take advantage of whatever winds are blowing to increase air speed over their wings by taking off and landing into the wind. And planes have all kinds of slots to increase lift.

But even with all these aids, takeoff is still difficult. A jet plane's powerful engines must still send it roaring down the runway until it is going fast enough so that the speed of the air over its wings produces enough lift. Only when lift exceeds the pull of gravity can the plane be drawn up and away from the earth.

Birds were using all these different ways to increase lift long before airplanes were invented, long before man appeared on earth. They can change their wing size, lower flaps, open slots, and rev up the speed of their propellers by beating their wings faster. They take advantage of available wind, too. Almost all birds usually take off into the wind, and some birds must do it. Any extra movement of air above their wings will give them extra lift. All these special techniques are necessary because getting up into the air requires so much more energy than does merely staying up there.

Condors' wings are so long they would strike the ground during ordinary takeoffs, so these birds begin and end their flights on cliffs.

The Problem of the Condors

The larger birds usually find it more difficult to get into the air. South American condors are the biggest flying birds on the American continent, with wings that may be nine and a half feet across. Though wings this large supply a great amount of lift during flight, their length becomes a problem during takeoff. The condor cannot flap its wings very far without hitting the ground. This reduces the amount of lift so much that the bird simply can't get airborne without some kind of outside help. On level ground, it must have a strong wind that it can face to give it additional lift. If the air is still, the bird is grounded.

Knowing this, South American natives often catch condors by baiting quiet valleys with appealing foods. If a bird lands, it cannot get out again without a breeze. Usually, condors try to avoid this problem by landing in high places such as cliffs, where they can leap into the air to start their next flight. The giant condors are a good example of a general principle: the heavier a bird is, the greater its need for some kind of outside help to get it off the ground.

Other Aids to Takeoff

Some birds create the extra power needed for takeoff by rotating their wings at the shoulders. Instead of moving up and down, the wings move back and forth almost horizontally. Although it takes enormous energy to do this, it produces so much lift that the bird rises into the air more like a helicopter than a conventional plane.

Open slots are commonly used to increase lift during takeoff. When the alulas attached to the thumbs at the front of the wings are opened, slots are formed that force the air to speed up as it squeezes through them. This faster-moving air over the wings increases lift. Some birds can't produce enough lift for takeoff without the help of this slotting.

Another method for getting into the air is to shoot up into it. If a bird's legs are similar to those of the long-legged heron. it can use them to great advantage. The heron shoves itself away from the ground with its long legs so that there is plenty of room for its wings to make their first downward flap. Some ducks get the same result by suddenly pushing against the water with their wings.

But most of the water birds, such as geese and swans, loons, grebes, and diving ducks, need very long runs on the surface of the water before they manage to achieve flight speed. Their large, webbed feet make it possible for them to pound along the top of the water. The heavier the bird or the smaller its wings, the faster the bird will have to be running before it lifts off from the water or ground. This running technique works on any surface. Of course, the stronger the headwind, the less running any bird will have to do.

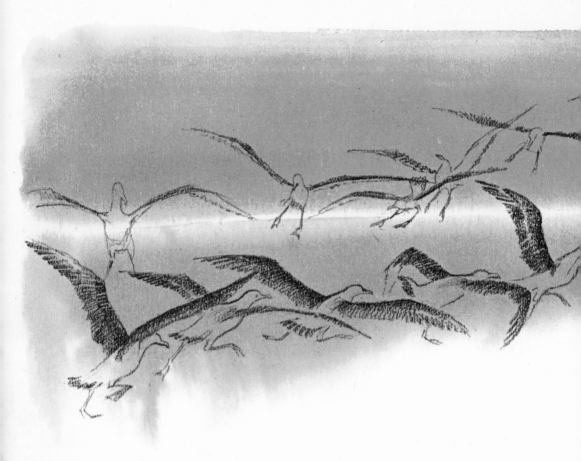

Young gooney birds run clumsily down the beaches of Midway Island trying to get up enough speed for lift-off. Without additional breeze, their landings are as awkward as their takeoffs and often end with the birds comically skidding to a stop on their bellies.

Gooney Takeoffs

Birds that are excellent gliders often have trouble during takeoff and landing, for large wings cannot be moved too quickly. Examples of these birds are the albatrosses that live around Midway Island in the Pacific Ocean. These birds are surely among the most graceful creatures in all the Wild Kingdom. They are masters at riding the ocean breezes and thermals, and sail for hours without ever moving their wings. These particular albatrosses

were affectionately renamed "gooney birds" by the sailors stationed at Midway Island during World War II. This name was partly a result of their funny courting behavior.

But it also refers to the way they take off and land. For while the enormous area of their wings produces great lift even at low speeds, gooney birds have become so dependent on gliding that their takeoff techniques leave much to be desired.

When the young gooney birds are first learning to fly, it sometimes seems as if they'll never get up enough power to leave the ground. For a while, they

Running furiously on the water, this swan must achieve a certain speed before enough lift forms above its wings to get it airborne.

stand in one place on the beach, instinctively facing the wind and timidly flapping their wings. Gradually, they move them faster and faster, with more and more confidence, similar to planes revving up their engines at the end of a runway. But that doesn't work either. Some try hopping into the air, then a combination of hopping and flapping. Finally, they begin running across the flat beaches, beating the air furiously, trying to produce enough lift to take them away from the ground.

Eventually, the young gooneys do get into the air. The breezes are usually steady and strong around these ocean islands, and the gooneys' long, narrow wings take advantage of the free lift provided by these winds. High

in the air, everything is fine. Hour after hour they glide effortlessly on outstretched wings, seldom moving them. Unfortunately, there comes that moment when the bird must face the problem of getting down again.

Gooney Landings

Relying on breezes and thermals is fine when the bird is way up, but it becomes risky business as it begins to descend. The closer the bird gets to earth, the slower the wind moves, and the weaker the updrafts become. The gooney begins losing altitude, gently at first, then more and more quickly. Finally, there is no updraft at all, the extra lift from the wind disappears, and the gooney skids in for a landing on its beak, surely the most spectacularly clumsy landing in all birddom. A moment later, however, it straightens itself up, gets back on its feet, and waddles off with as much dignity as a gooney bird can muster. And this appears to be a very great amount, indeed.

Braking and Landing

Landing is more complicated and difficult than takeoff, even for the best of flyers. Stopping any object going at great speed without damaging it is always tricky. A fresh egg falling through the air is perfectly safe—until its flight is stopped too suddenly by the ground. Planes, spacecraft, and birds all must end their flights gently. And, obviously, the heavier the bird or plane and the greater its speed, the more difficult a safe landing becomes.

At the start of a landing, the bird lets itself down from the sky by slowing or stopping its propellers, that is, by slowing or stopping its wing beats. When this happens, the bird's forward speed through the air is reduced. So is lift. Gravity then begins pulling the bird toward earth. If the bird is gliding with outstretched wings, the propeller feathers at the ends of the wing are no longer working to drive the bird forward. Instead, they add

to the surface area of the wing and so create more lift to help slow the bird's fall toward earth. Gently, the bird glides downward.

As the bird's forward speed slows still more, its wings rotate slightly at the shoulders, increasing their angle of attack to create still more lift and prevent the bird from dropping too quickly. The tail may be spread open and lowered to act as a brake against the air. Now the feet are forward, ready to grab the target branch. To slow it still more, the wings may be cupped like a parachute. The slots are opened to prevent stalling, that sudden loss of lift that could send the bird crashing to the ground.

If the bird is still approaching its target too quickly, it can throw its propellers into reverse. By twisting its wings at the shoulders slightly, air pressure automatically bends the outer primaries up at the tips. Now when the wings swing forward, these feathers strike the air in just the opposite way from which they do normally. They begin propelling in reverse, and this acts as a further brake to the bird's forward motion.

The moment of impact is still a dangerous one! The intended branch may suddenly move in the wind. A gust of wind may roll the bird, and a flutter of wings will be needed to make a last-second correction. If the bird is already among the branches, the wings must be moved carefully to avoid damaging them. At last the feet lock onto the branch and the strong leg muscles absorb the final shock of impact. The flight is over. The bird has made a remarkable and dangerous transition from air to earth safely. It has all happened so quickly that no human eye, unaided by a high-speed camera, could really see it, could be aware of how complicated and beautiful these few seconds actually are. We see birds take off and land every day, and still we do not really see them.

Chapter 7

MODIFICATION FOR FLIGHT

FLIGHT is so remarkable that it takes a whole series of special physical modifications before an animal can accomplish it. Before birds could fly, millions of years passed in which the scales of their reptilian ancestors gradually were replaced by feathers and their front legs replaced by wings. Other changes, too, had to occur before flight was possible, for flight is much more than just feathers and wings. For example, no matter how many feathers a man might attach to his arms or how furiously he might flap them, he still could not overcome the pull of gravity in the same way birds do—and for a good reason: man is too heavy. Gravity pulls too strongly at his solid body and the thick bones needed to support it. His muscles simply are not big enough to supply the energy needed to lift such weight.

Archaeopteryx *is the earliest bird known to us; 140 million years ago, it floundered in the mud and died, leaving not only a fossil record of its bones, but an imprint of its feathers as well.*

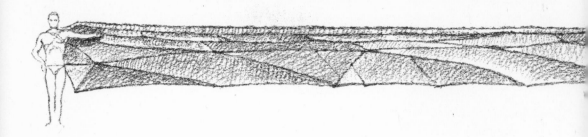

To supply enough lift for man's great weight, wings 140-feet long would be needed. Stresses would be so enormous that flapping wings this large would be almost impossible.

Reduced Size

Attaching wings to elephants or horses or men still does not make it possible for them to fly, for the heavier an animal is, the larger its wings must be to produce enough aerodynamic lift to support it. And the larger the wings are, the more muscle needed to move them. These larger muscles in turn add their weight to the animal, which means still more lift is needed to raise the animal from the ground. And around and around the problem goes.

In addition, the larger the wing becomes, the more resistance it meets moving through the air. Just try swinging a large flat object quickly against the air. A giant bird would have the same trouble moving its wings. As its huge muscles strained to overcome the resistance of the air to its giant wings, stresses on the wing itself would become so great that the wing would shatter. The materials that animals

are made of are remarkable, but they are not strong enough to build a giant bird. This puts a severe limit on just how heavy a flapping bird can be.

The largest and heaviest birds flying today are the great bustard of Europe and the Australian bustard. They can weigh as much as thirty-two pounds and be nearly four feet long. The largest bird that we know ever flew is now extinct, but its bones were found in Nevada. Its scientific name is *Teratornis incredibilis*. Its wingspread was nearly seventeen feet. But seventeen feet is still a long way from the giant flying animals of legend and science fiction.

There have been truly giant birds, but we know of none that could fly. Even today, some of these great birds are scattered about our earth. The largest living species is the ostrich, but its eight-foot height is not the record. The extinct giant moa of New Zealand once stood twelve feet tall and weighed seven hundred pounds. The elephant bird of Madagascar was not

Three-hundred-pound ostriches, extinct seven-hundred-pound moas and men are way above the weight at which flapping flight is possible.

quite as tall, but weighed even more, about nine hundred pounds. Although all of these giant birds were flightless, they clearly had descended from smaller ancestors that had been able to fly. After the millions and millions of years it took for flying animals to evolve, how was it possible that some of them lost this remarkable ability of flight?

The most probable explanation for this loss is that long ago life got too easy for some of their ancestors. The competition for food was not fierce enough, and they found enough to eat on the ground. There were few enemies to chase them into the air, or even to prevent them from nesting on the ground. Over a long period of time, a certain number of mutations appeared. Some of these imperfect copies might have had smaller wings. Normally, this would have made it so difficult for them to get food or escape danger that they couldn't have survived. But in these unusually comfortable conditions, flight was no longer essential. The birds of these areas were doing less and less of it. Some of these "handicapped" birds did as well as the "normal" birds—and were able to reproduce.

Since these birds were no longer flying, there was no longer any reason for them not to grow larger and larger. Walking and running were now the principal means of locomotion, so the hind legs became heavier and stronger. Generation after generation passed, with a long succession of mutations, until giant birds finally appeared. The

African ostrich is the largest of these great birds surviving today—and weighs three hundred pounds, which is far beyond the weight limit imposed by flapping flight. To fly, an animal must be light. The easiest way to be light is to be small.

Reduced Weight

There is another method, however, to make a flying machine light, and that is to build it with lighter materials. This is more complicated, for great care must be taken not to lose, along with the loss in weight, any of the strength needed for flight.

Birds have a number of special lightweight construction materials. Feathers are one of them. Adding very little to the bird's weight, feathers create the smooth, hard, streamlined surfaces that slip easily through the air and produce the necessary aerodynamic lift. Wings, in fact, are almost entirely feathers, with only a few bones along the leading edges.

Those bones a bird does have are also designed for lightness. Instead of being mostly solid, like those of ground-hugging animals, many of a bird's bones are hollow and filled with air. This makes them light, but surprisingly does not reduce their strength. An example of how something can be strong

A bird's actual body is smaller than it appears beneath the fluffy feathers; in addition it is full of large air sacs.

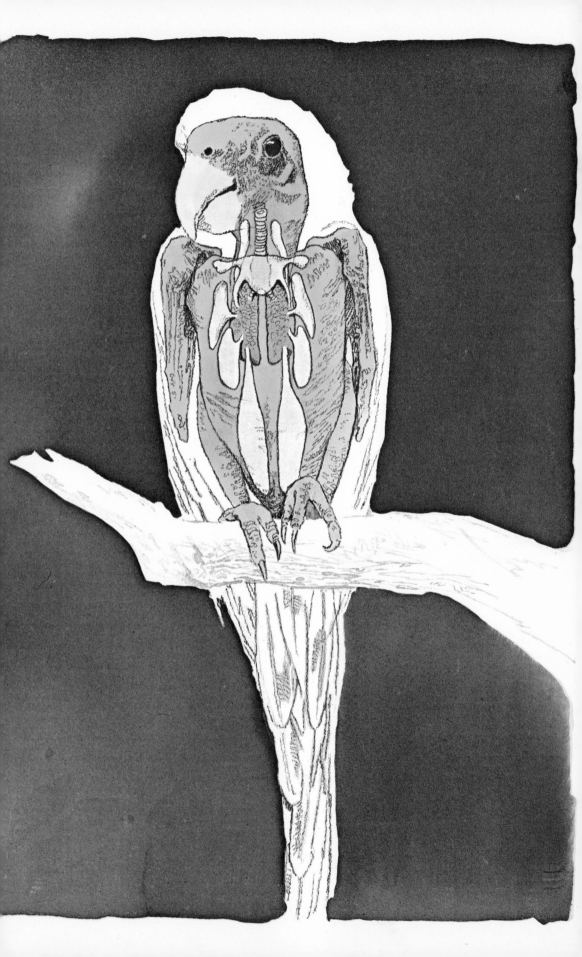

without being solid is a corrugated box. The stiff cardboard of these boxes is made of half circles of paper sandwiched between two sheets of paper. As strong as this cardboard is, it is almost completely hollow.

Bent or braced materials are often stronger for their weight than solid materials. The steel girders that support giant buildings are I-shaped, L-shaped, H-shaped, but seldom solid chunks of metal. The swings in a playground are suspended from hollow pipes, the climbing bars of a Junglegym are made of hollow pipes, the seesaw rests on a hollow pipe. So the hollow bones of a bird can, and obviously do, provide all the strength needed with far less weight than solid ones would.

Some birds have bones that are even further adapted for the stresses of flight, with diagonally placed struts inside them. These lightweight braces are very much like the ones men use in the construction of houses and bridges and our own flying machines.

Birds conserve weight in other ways. Most warm-blooded animals have their brains carefully protected inside a thick and heavy case, the skull. But not birds. They have dropped much of this extra weight in favor of an almost paper-thin skull. Their impressive-looking beaks are deceptive too: the enormous one of the toucan isn't nearly as heavy or solid as it appears. The toucan's bill is actually made of extremely light and porous layers of bony material.

Lightness is essential for flight, and a fairly good indication of just how well a particular bird can fly is a comparison of the weight of its bones with the rest of its body. The very best gliding and soaring birds have the lightest skeletons; some have bones that weigh less than their feathers! The powerful flying birds have medium-weight skeletons. The nonflying birds, like the ostrich, have the heaviest bone structures of all.

If you have ever handled a bird, you know how surprisingly light it is. Hidden under all its fluffy feathers, a bird's body is really much smaller than it appears. And hidden inside that small body are many large sacs filled with air, making the bird even lighter than if these spaces were filled with solid materials. If a boy and a duck were the same size, the duck would weigh only half as much as the boy. The special designs that make a bird light are basic to any flying machine, natural or man-made. Overcoming the pull of gravity is difficult enough without having to carry along any more weight than is absolutely necessary.

Reduced Number of Moving Parts

There are many ways to get rid of extra weight; one is to cut down the number of heavy muscles needed. In man, for example, many muscles spend most of their time simply holding the flexible backbone erect. Large, heavy muscles in the back and legs are re-

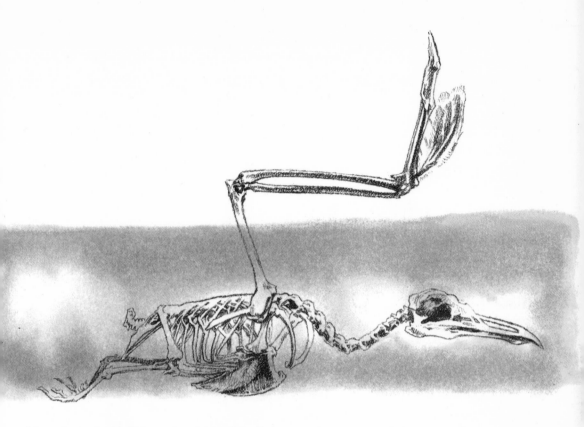

Many bones in birds have fused together. Fewer moving parts need fewer muscles to hold them in special positions.

quired to keep the hinged torso upright. In birds, many bones have no joints between them, but are permanently fused together. This eliminates the need for special muscles to hold them in any particular position. The fusing of some bones and the elimination of many others makes the skeleton of a bird more rigid than a man's. But it also means that most of the big muscles a bird carries aloft can concentrate on the difficult job of moving its wings during flight.

Increased Muscular Development

Animals that cannot fly do not have the right muscles in the right places for flying. Man's principle means of natural locomotion is walking, so it is not surprising to find our largest muscles in our legs. We don't use our arms to swing from the trees or flap them to push us through the air. So most of us don't have enormously developed arm muscles. A reasonably strong person can pull his body away from the ground with his arms a few times by chinning himself, but as anyone knows who has done this, it takes considerable effort and cannot be done many times.

It's a little easier for us to push our bodies away from the ground with push-ups. Most of us can do this providing our arms are directly beneath us. But if we try spreading our arms out in a birdlike position, most of us cannot lift our body weight even once —the average person's chest muscles simply are not developed enough. Yet when a bird takes off from the ground and rises into the air, it has lifted its entire body weight with its chest muscles. Here, two great sets of muscles, called the major and minor pectorals, move its wings. In man, the chest muscles account for about 1 per cent of

his weight. In birds, the chest muscles are 15 per cent of the bird's entire weight, sometimes even more. Few of the muscles that move the wings are located in the wings themselves, for this would only increase the weight of the wings and make them more difficult to move. Instead, most of a bird's muscles are in the breast and are connected to the wings by long, cordlike tendons.

The largest of these pectoral muscles move the wings during the downstroke. One end of each of these muscles is attached to the *keel*, or breastbone, of the bird; the other end, to a tendon that hooks to the underside of each wing. When these muscles contract, the wing is pulled downward. Since this downstroke produces almost all the power for flight, the major pectorals are often ten times larger than the minor pectorals. These

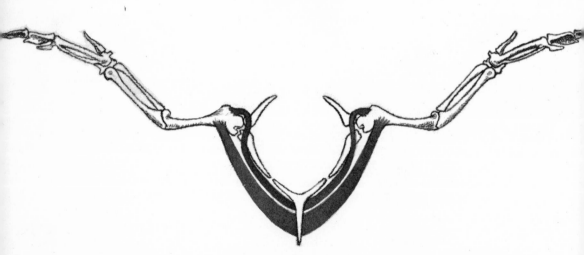

Large outside breast muscles pull wings down. An inner set attached to wing tops by pulley-like tendons pulls wings up.

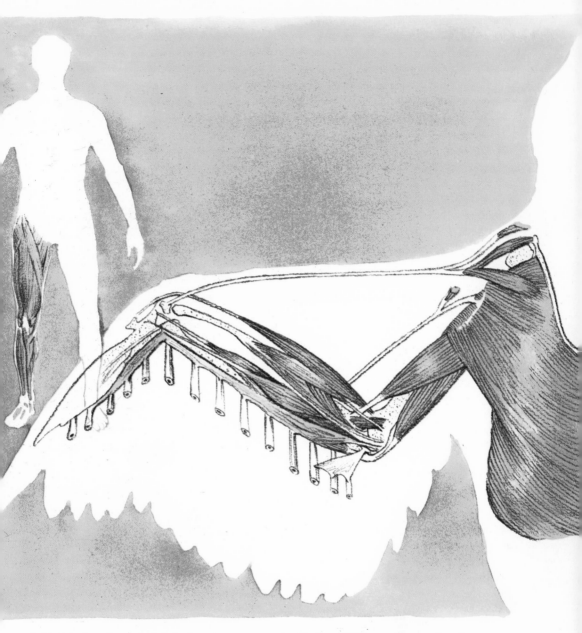

A bird is heavily muscled in its chest, a man in his legs. This explains why pigeons cannot run very fast and men cannot fly.

Extra weight can make flight impossible. Depositing their eggs quickly in a nest relieves birds of this extra baggage.

smaller muscles that raise the wings are also attached at one end to the keel of the bird. But in order to pull the wings up, they must somehow be attached to the top of the wings. They are— by means of a long tendon that passes over the shoulder like a rope over a pulley.

Since most of the muscles needed for flight are attached to the keel of a bird, this bone has become strengthened and enlarged to provide room for such attachment. Generally, the size of this keel is a good indication of the flying power of a bird. The larger the keel, the more wing muscles the bird probably has. Nonflying birds don't have greatly developed pectoral muscles and they don't have large keels either. The walking ostrich has its main muscles in its legs, just as man has.

Not all the muscles of a flying bird are for flight, since most birds not only fly but walk and hop (and some even swim). Therefore, most birds have not only enormous flight muscles, but they usually have well-developed leg muscles too.

Reduced Baggage

Even the bird's system for reproduction is especially suited to the weight requirements of flight. Mammals evolved a reproductive system in which the developing offspring is protected for some time by being inside the body of its mother. Birds, however, have kept the reptilian system of egg-laying, but with this modification: they protect the eggs in a nest while the embryos develop inside.

For a flying animal, laying eggs provides a weight advantage over the mammalian system of carrying the embryo. It doesn't take long for an egg to form: a chicken egg develops from start to finish in just twenty-six hours. As soon as a bird egg is finished, it leaves the mother's body and is left in a nest. In mammals, however, the egg is kept inside the body while the next stages of development take place. By getting rid of the egg before this happens, the bird greatly shortens the amount of time that it is hampered by this extra weight. In birds, the major and time-consuming part of embryo development takes place outside the mother's body.

But the egg-laying techniques of birds are not exactly like most other egg-layers. For example, birds don't collect large numbers of fully developed eggs in their abdomen before depositing them, as fish and most reptiles do. If more than one egg is to be laid, the bird produces them more or less in an assembly-line fashion. As quickly as one is completed, shell and all, it is deposited in the nest. This system, like so many of the other special modifications of birds, helps keep them at flying weight most of the time.

Improved Vision

A high-speed animal like a bird must have excellent vision. It must be able to judge distances accurately to make safe landings, or to catch insects in the air. Birds that hunt during the day must be able to distinguish colors.

A man looking at a field mouse might see it like this.

From the same distance, a bird would see the mouse much more clearly.

A bird whose eyes look out from opposite sides of the head sees more at the same time than a bird with paired eyes in front.

Night birds must be able to see in dim light. The large, high-flying birds of prey need to see great distances. Of all the animals in the Wild Kingdom, birds have perhaps the best vision— even better than man's. The part of their brain that deals with vision is proportionately larger than it is in any other animal. The eyes of some birds are so large that they weigh more than the animal's brain.

Some birds have both eyes placed in front, the same as we do. In this position, both eyes see the same thing at the same time. But many more birds have their eyes placed on opposite sides of the head. In this position, each eye is facing a different direction and is actually looking at a different scene. With its eyes placed this way, the bird is able to see more different things at any given instant than we can.

Perhaps because it does see so much more, a bird's eyes do not need to be as movable as ours. If a bird is look-ing for something that is not already in its field of view, it cannot turn just its eyes but must cock its entire head around. A bird's neck is extremely flexible, so this is easily done. A bird's eyes are different from ours in other ways, too. They have two more eye-lids than we do. The upper eyelid is very much like ours, but there is also a lower one, which we do not have. The lower lid is usually the one closed when the bird is sleeping. In addition, there is a transparent third eyelid that sweeps horizontally across the eye, cleaning the surface like a windshield wiper. This third lid may also be used to protect the eye against wind when the bird is flying, and in at least some birds it acts as an extra lens.

When both eyes are placed forward on the face, as ours are, so that the two eyes see approximately the same thing at the same time, we call it *binocular* vision. The prefix *bi* means two. Owls have eyes like this, and so see the world in the same way we do. But most other birds have their eyes farther back on the sides of the head so that each eye has a much greater field of vision. When only one eye views something, this is called *monocular* vision. *Mono* means one.

The obvious advantage of having eyes on either side of the head is that it allows the bird to see danger ap-proaching from more directions at the same time. The disadvantage of mo-nocular vision is that it provides a flat view of the world. It's a two-di-mensional view like that of a picture printed on a flat sheet of paper. And this may restrict an animal's ability to judge distances accurately.

It is hard to imagine what the world looks like to a bird—covering one of your eyes will not immediately give you an idea of what monocular vision is really like. But you would soon enough notice the difference if you tried a game like horseshoes or ring toss. When one eye is covered, the only clues left to tell your muscles how far away the peg is are the size of the peg and your memory of where it is. If you were trying to judge how near some new object was, memory ob-

viously couldn't help, so you'd have to judge its distance from you by its size alone. Generally, the larger something is, the closer it is. But not always. Judging distances with one eye is extremely difficult.

Looking at the same object with both eyes, however, gives us a very good idea of how far away it is. An exaggerated example of how objects stand out from one another in binocular vision is the effect you get from stereoscopic, or three-dimensional, slides or pictures. With one eye looking at the same scene as the other eye, but a few inches to the side, near objects dramatically separate from the distant objects behind them.

Actually, this stereoscopic vision is the kind we humans enjoy every day. So do many birds, even some of those with eyes spaced far apart. These birds have the advantages of both kinds of vision, monocular and binocular. They not only can see an enormous expanse of the world about them in two dimensions, but where the fields of view from each eye overlap in front, they see that part of the world in three dimensions.

The ultimate in wide-angle vision is found in the woodcock, a medium-sized bird that feeds on worms. It hunts for its food in the mud, feeling around for the worms with its bill. Its eyes are not in front or to the side, but

A woodcock's eyes are so far back it sees in a complete circle. Where views overlap slightly, it sees three-dimensionally.

are rather far back on the top of its head. This makes the woodcock look a little strange to us, but it also makes it possible for it to go about its business searching for food in the mud and still see any approaching danger, even behind it. The woodcock can see in almost all directions at the same time!

There is no way for us to experience a view of the world as the woodcock sees it. It is even a little hard to imagine. Where the vision of its two eyes overlap in front and back, the bird has three-dimensional vision. The rest of the way around, the woodcock has to make do with only a two-dimensional view of the world.

In a certain sense photographs are better copies of the world than the original we see with our eyes. Actually, the world never really looks like a sharply focused photograph to us; only one small part of any scene registers in great detail at any given moment. Everything else is seen only vaguely. If we focus our vision on the letters of this printed page, the rest of the room will be out of focus. If we look up suddenly to see a man entering the room, the book will go out of focus as the man is brought into focus.

In birds, however, the eyeball is much flatter than ours. Besides saving space and weight, this design tends to keep more of any scene in focus at the same time. When any additional change of focus is required, it is done by muscles that actually bend the lens in each eye. For a distant object, the lens is flat. To bring something nearby into sharp focus, the lens is squeezed

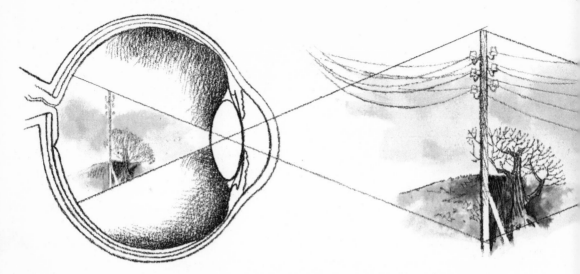

Birds' eyes are more tightly packed with light-sensitive receivers than human eyes, which makes it possible for them to see details more clearly than we can. From the same distance, the individual telephone lines would tend to blur together with the background in the human eye (left), while the bird's eye (right) would see them as individual lines.

into a rounder shape. This is very much the way our own eyes operate except that the muscles that do the lens-bending for birds are often faster and stronger than our own. In some birds, the lens may actually be softer than ours. These differences make it possible for a bird to change focus much more quickly than a human can.

In addition, some birds can bend these lenses farther than we can. They are capable of bringing objects just a few inches away from them sharply into focus—something we humans normally cannot do with our stiffer lenses. A fishing bird like the cormorant has a range of focus perhaps four times greater than that of a human.

There are still other focusing tricks that birds can use. Some of the diving birds have a lenslike window in their third eyelids that acts as an additional lens. Hawks and owls may possibly be able to bend the transparent outer covering of their eyes in addition to the inner lenses. If this is true, having two adjustable lenses would be like having a built-in zoom lens in each eye.

Finally, the fact that birds have large eyes is important, for vision depends on how much information the optical system can gather together. The larger the lens, the more details both an eye and a camera can see. The unusually large eyes of birds, therefore, are very much like the oversized lenses and cameras used in reconnaissance planes and satellites.

The information that passes through the lens of an eye is focused onto the back part of the eyeball—the *retina.*

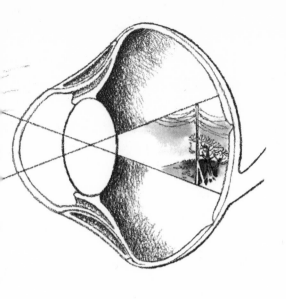

These light receptors at the back of the eye are of two types. The cones are sensitive to different colors, and operate best in bright light when all the colors are present. The rods are able to receive very weak light signals, but are not sensitive to color. It is not surprising, then, to find that the eyes of nocturnal birds, those that do their hunting at night, are equipped with more rods than those of the birds that hunt in daylight.

Bird Brains

The idea that "bird-brained" means stupid is a misconception. The brains of birds are developed for the kind of life they lead. Their centers for vision exceed ours. Their hearing is also highly developed, and the ear not only receives sound signals, but a part of it is also responsible for maintaining balance. In a free-moving animal such as the bird, balance requires critical control. And because flight is such a complicated series of muscular motions, the part of the brain responsible for coordinating and controlling the muscles is extraordinarily well developed.

(In a camera, the film corresponds to this part of the eye.) The retina is the image-detecting part of the eye and transforms the light signals that enter the eye into electrochemical signals that it sends on to the brain. There these signals are unscrambled and interpreted as a picture of the world outside the bird.

The retina of a bird's eye is twice as thick as man's and contains many more of these light-sensitive receptors, called *rods* and *cones*. This means the bird detects more details than we do. It has been calculated that a sparrow hawk sees about eight times more clearly than a man. From the same height that a hawk would be able to tell that two parallel paint strips down the center of a road were two distinct lines, our eyes would see a single line.

Birds can fly because over the course of millions and millions of years they have evolved the special equipment needed for flight. Each part of their body is modified especially to this end —including their brain. To watch the result of all these special modifications is to see a very remarkable and very beautiful part of the Wild Kingdom —the flight of birds.

Chapter 8

THE ENERGY SYSTEM

EVEN with all their special muscular and structural adaptations, birds have another major problem before flight is possible. Any flying machine that's heavier than air will use more energy to climb fifty feet upward against the pull of gravity than it will to move fifty feet forward. It doesn't matter whether it is a man-made device or a bird or how efficiently it is designed, it requires an enormous amount of energy to get up into the air.

But there is a double catch to this in the case of birds. These warm-blooded animals also use their power plants to keep warm. They must keep their bodies at a certain temperature —or die. You would think that small animals such as birds wouldn't have any trouble keeping warm. But the smaller an animal is, the more trouble it has staying warm. The reason is that, the smaller any object is, the more rapidly it loses heat. A cup of tea loses heat faster than a pot of tea.

[98]

So, the small bird uses up energy at an enormous rate just keeping warm. On the other hand, the large, heavy bird uses more energy overcoming the pull of gravity. Whatever the size of the bird, its power plant must supply all the energy it needs for warmth. Since this power plant also has to supply enough energy for the bird to lift itself, the lighter the power plant, the better.

If the power plant in any flying machine is too heavy, it may not be able to produce enough force to lift its own weight plus that of the flying machine. That was the problem with man's early attempts at flight—he tried to use his own muscles for power. Any gadget that uses muscle power has to fail because man simply cannot develop enough power to push even his own weight away from earth, let alone his own weight plus that of the flying apparatus. If he were ever going to fly, man would need an extremely lightweight, outside source of power.

The invention of the wood-burning steam engine didn't help him much. The amount of energy this engine produced was still too small compared to its weight. Replacing the wood fuel with coal was a great improvement, but the total energy output still wasn't enough to push a flying device away from the ground. It was only after the discovery of the concentrated energy in oil, and the invention of the internal combustion engine to release it, that the first heavier-than-air plane took off at Kitty Hawk.

Since then, fuels and engines have

The farther man moves away from the earth, the more energy he needs to do it. Fuel may be half of a jet's weight at takeoff, a thousand times the weight of a moon-landing craft.

constantly been improved. The development of the jet engine made even more power available for flight. Rocket engines and the exotic fuels they burn deliver still more energy for each pound of weight. The machines they power are able to fly higher and faster than ever before. Flights beyond this planet require even greater concentrations of energy. And so the search continues for still-lighter power plants that can produce even more energy per pound.

Birds solved the problem of energy production for flight more than 130 million years ago. During the millennia that followed, design improvements were continually made until today this equipment is so efficient that a bird not much bigger than a robin can fly 2,400 miles nonstop. This is the American golden plover—and it arrives in South America—after its remarkable trip across the open ocean—weighing only two ounces less than it did when it took off from Labrador.

Essentially, the way in which birds produce the great power needed for flight is by running their engines at top speed. This speed-up of their energy-producing machinery has the same effect that running any machine too fast has—it shortens the life of the machine. Most songbirds, under natural conditions, live less than two years.

A bird's entire body is designed for lightness, and this dictates even the kinds of foods it uses for fuel. Birds concentrate on "high-octane" foods that contain the greatest amount of releasable energy for their weight. Foods such as seeds, fruits, fish, and even insects and rodents, are rich in calories. Most birds ignore low-calorie foods like leaves or grass, for the bird would have to eat much greater amounts of these foods to get the same amount of calories. The bird would be carrying more weight and getting less energy from it.

Even these high-energy foods are quickly used up by a bird's fast-running machinery. Some young birds eat their own weight in food each day, and certain adult birds may eat almost that much. Compare that to what you eat each day, or to what a dog or a horse or an elephant eats.

Part of the reason birds need so much food is their small size. And the smaller they are, the faster they use up this food in replacing body heat. The speed at which a tiny hummingbird burns its food in relation to its body weight is fifty times that of man! Small birds, therefore, need super-amounts of superfuels just to stay alive.

During the day, most birds are able to keep replacing the food they use up. But many birds can't search for food in the dark. If a certain kind of mountain hummingbird continued burning fuel during the night at the same rate it did during the day, it would starve to death before morning! These particular hummingbirds survive the dark by slowing down the speed at which they live. Their heartbeats slow down, breathing is reduced, and their temperatures drop. In this *torpid* state, their bodies require less food. This enables them to survive a temporary food shortage in much the same way that *hibernation* helps other animals survive a temporary food shortage during the cold of winter.

Birds are able to "eat and run." Most other animals must tear a meal into small pieces before they can swallow it, but the extremely thin wall of

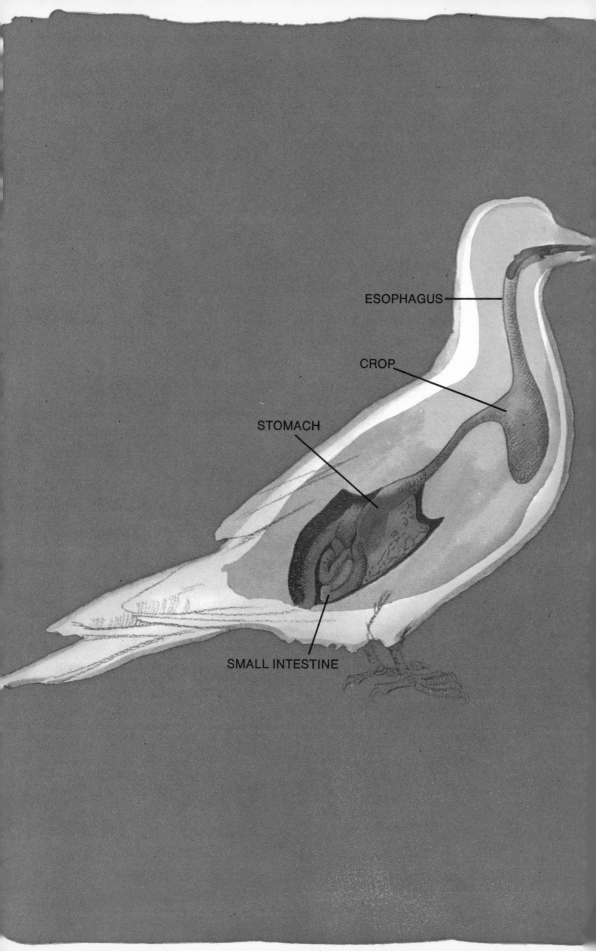

ESOPHAGUS

CROP

STOMACH

SMALL INTESTINE

a bird's esophagus stretches to let very large mouthfuls pass down. The bird can grab its meal, then quickly fly out of danger.

Some birds are not even bothered with a meal too big to fit into their stomachs. We humans suffer if the tiniest piece of food gets stuck in our throats, but a bird may have the head of a fish safely in its stomach while the tail is still sticking out its mouth. In some kinds of birds, the lower end of the esophagus has developed into a permanently expanded storage area known as the *crop*. Food can be held in the crop for hours. In some cases, it acts as a sort of first stomach, and the food can be softened and predigested there before it moves on.

Once the food enters the first part of the real stomach, digestive juices pour over it. These chemicals begin to dissolve the bonds that hold the food together. In the gizzard, the lower part of the stomach, muscles mix the food thoroughly with the powerful digestive juices, crushing it and helping to tear it apart. In some birds the muscles of the gizzard are powerful enough to crush a tin can. Since birds have no teeth, those that eat hard grains usually swallow pebbles or bits

The digestive system (green) is a long, bulging, twisting tube that breaks large chunks of food into pieces small enough for the body to use for growth and energy. Food enters one end, is pushed, pulled and kneaded by the stomach, and torn apart chemically by acids in the stomach and alkalies in the small intestine.

of shell along with their food to help the gizzard in this grinding process. These "stomach teeth" eventually get worn down themselves. When they're too small, the bird gets rid of them with its other waste materials. Then it must swallow a new supply.

Chemical breakdown of the food continues as it moves on to the small intestine. When it is finally molecule size, the food is absorbed through the wall of the intestine into the bloodstream and transported to all the cells of the animal's body.

This fuel-refining process operates at a fantastic rate in birds: in some, a berry can be completely digested in twenty minutes. Not only is bird digestion rapid, but it is also more complete in birds than in other animals. Compared with mammals, growing birds are able to use three times as much of the food they eat for energy and growth. The small amount of material that cannot be used is quickly disposed of, and the birds remain as light as possible. They have practically no structures for the storage of waste materials. In some of the larger birds that eat their prey whole, as owls and kingfishers, the indigestible bones and fur and scales never even get to the lower part of the digestive system. Instead, they're quickly coughed up from the stomach in little pellets.

This high-speed processing plant is able to dump into the bloodstream large amounts of ready-to-burn fuel as quickly as it is needed. But birds use this fuel so quickly that the hopper must be refilled constantly. As a result,

The smaller a warm-blooded animal is, the more food (represented by boxes) it eats in proportion to its weight.

birds spend most of their lives looking for food.

To release energy from fuels such as coal and gasoline and food, they must be *burned*. This process of *combustion* combines the molecules of the fuel with those of *oxygen* and rearranges them into new materials. As these chemical changes take place, some of the energy that formerly held the molecules together is released in the form of heat. Therefore, to free the energy from the foods the bird has eaten, a supply of oxygen is needed.

Actually, the more oxygen that is available, the faster the fuel will burn. For example, as more air containing oxygen is pumped against the coals in a blacksmith's forge, the faster and hotter they burn. In the old days, this pumping was done by hand-operated bellows. In modern furnaces, air is blown in by enormous fans. Aircraft and racing-car engines are *supercharged* in this same way by forcing air into their combustion chambers. Men and birds have air pumped into their bodies by bellows-like devices called lungs.

Once inside the body, oxygen passes from the air through the walls of the lungs into the bloodstream. (This happens in much the same way that molecules of food pass through the walls of the intestine into the moving blood.) Here the oxygen combines with passing red corpuscles and is transported to each cell of the body.

It is inside the cells that oxygen finally combines with the food. This chemical reaction releases the energy the cells need for life and the materials they need for growth. When the burn-ing is finished, leftover materials from the combustion are dumped from the cells into the bloodstream. The carbon dioxide waste moves back up to the lungs and is finally pumped out of the body into the air. This much is the same in both men and birds.

Pumping in the great quantities of air needed and pumping out the waste gases require a very efficient system. The lungs of a bird are not proportionately any larger than those of a man, but the bird has an additional system of unique air sacs that we humans do not have. A man's lungs might fill about 5 per cent of his body, but in some cases the lungs and air sacs of a bird might occupy 20 per cent of its body. These large sacs are connected to the lungs and extend throughout the body, even entering the hollow portions of some of the bigger bones. These air sacs help lighten the bird, of course, and they also greatly increase the amount of air always inside the animal.

In addition to the greater size of the bird's air system, its lungs can operate faster than ours. At rest, a man breathes about sixteen times a minute; during the most strenuous exercise he can increase his oxygen intake five or six times. A pigeon at rest breathes about twenty-nine times a minute; that same pigeon in flight breathes 450 times a minute!

Speed and size are only part of the story: the way a bird's lungs operate is different from ours too. For example, birds never run out of breath as men do. Instead, they fly into breath. The difference is interesting. To make our lungs expand and draw in fresh, oxygen-containing air, we contract a great, muscular diaphragm just below our rib cage. When we relax that muscle, the rib cage automatically springs back to its normal size and we exhale. Birds breathe in exactly the opposite manner. They use their muscular effort to get rid of the stale air, so when they relax, fresh air is automatically *drawn in*.

In addition, birds do not have a *separate* muscular diaphragm to operate their lungs as we do, but conserve weight by using their chest muscles. In flight, as the pectoral muscles contract to move the wings, they press against the ribs and automatically force the bird to breathe faster as it flies faster. And with hardly any extra effort.

But the most striking difference of all between the respiratory systems of men and birds is the way in which the air moves through the two systems. Our lungs branch out like an upside-down tree. Fresh air moves down through the many branches as they get smaller and smaller until it reaches millions of tiny bags at the ends of these passages.

These very small *air sacs* in our lungs are not to be confused with the larger air sacs in birds, for they serve very different purposes. The sacs in our lungs are surrounded by many blood vessels, and here oxygen is pushed from the sacs into the blood and carbon dioxide is picked up from it. When we exhale, the stale air moves back out

the same paths the fresh air entered. We can never breathe in and out at the same time; we must first do one thing, stop, and only then can we reverse the process. In addition, we never really manage to get all the stale air out of our lungs when we exhale. There is always a small amount of it still caught in these tiny air sacs.

But birds' lungs don't have these dead ends to trap the stale air. Instead of moving alternately in and out of sacs, the air keeps moving along a system of tubes in one direction, generally speaking. Because these passages are tubes that are open on both ends instead of sacs with only one opening, the stale air can be flushed out of them much more efficiently. There is fresh air in a bird's lungs both when it breathes in and when it breathes out. Birds come the closest of any animal in nature to having the efficient, one-way air system of a jet engine. The smallest of these tubes are surrounded by blood vessels, and it is here that the oxygen moves into the blood and the carbon dioxide moves out.

To help keep the bird's energy requirements satisfied, the amounts of food and oxygen in the blood are concentrated. Birds have about twice the concentration of sugar for burning in their blood that we do. They don't have any more oxygen-carrying red corpuscles than men, but those they do have work more efficiently. Here's how their special system works.

There's a limit to how much oxygen will dissolve directly into the blood, just as there is a limit to how much carbon dioxide can be forced into water to make a bottle of carbonated soda pop. But the blood of both birds and men contains a material called hemoglobin. Atoms of oxygen gas attach themselves to the hemoglobin. Attached in this way, much more oxygen can be fit into the blood than if the gas were just dissolved in it. In order for the oxygen to get to the cells, however, it must eventually unhook itself from the hemoglobin. Birds' hemoglobin has a weaker hold on the oxygen than man's, so this unhooking takes place much faster in birds and more oxygen can be delivered to the cells.

To move this blood containing the large amounts of oxygen and food and carbon dioxide, a souped-up pumping system is needed. The pump itself must be large enough and strong enough to handle the job; just how large depends on the size of the bird and where it lives. The smaller the bird, the faster it loses heat to the outside air, so the larger its heart must be in relation to the rest of its body to make up for this. Birds (and humans) that live high in the mountains, where the air is thinner and the temperatures lower, have larger hearts to supply extra fuel and oxygen to their cells. Birds that live closer to the poles have larger hearts, too, for the colder temperatures there demand extra heat production. In general, however, all birds have relatively larger hearts than those of other animals.

Besides handling normal energy re-quirements, a bird's heart must have enough reserve capacity for the extreme requirements of takeoff and flight. To provide the greater amounts of blood per minute needed by all the cells, the heart must be able to speed up enormously. A bird's heart can beat faster than that of almost any other animal. Even resting, a small bird's heartbeat is fast: it might contract four hundred times a minute compared to a man's rate of seventy beats a minute. With this sort of furious pumping, blood makes a complete circuit of the bird's body in just seconds. In flight or other stress situations, the speed can increase to a thousand beats a minute. Again, the smaller the animal, the faster its heart works.

In addition, the whole circulatory system of birds operates under greater pressure than ours, and this extra pressure moves materials in and out of the cells faster. But it also puts dangerous stresses on the walls of the blood vessels: ruptures of the arteries are common in birds, and, as in man, are often fatal.

The by-product of all this energy-producing combustion is heat. In such a high-energy system, enormous quantities of it are produced. Birds are normally seven or eight degrees Fahrenheit hotter than men. In fact, they may be operating close to the very upper temperature limits possible for living things. For while it is true that too little heat kills, so does too much of it. A bird must be able to get rid of any excess heat that develops in its body, especially during the strenuous act of flying, for a very slight increase in body temperature is likely to cause death.

Excess heat is a problem in most energy systems. Most automobile engines would melt if they did not have a jacket of water circulating around them to carry the extra heat safely away. Aircraft engines (and some of the newer, smaller automobile engines) use a flow of air rather than water to take surplus heat away. An evaporation system carries man's extra heat away: he perspires. Moisture on the surface of his skin evaporates into the air and draws heat from his body, just as the water evaporating from a teakettle as steam draws heat from the water left in the kettle. Feathered birds don't have skin they can moisten—at least on the outside. So their principal means of cooling involves evaporation from the inside of their bodies.

A flow of air is essential for fast evaporation, and at least half of all the air taken in by a bird is used in this way to cool it. Moderate amounts of heat are evaporated from the upper parts of their lungs in much the same way as happens with dogs when they pant. During flight, however, the lung surfaces are not large enough to carry away the enormous amounts of excess heat formed, so the huge air sacs attached to the lungs become evaporators too. These bags are many times larger than the lungs themselves and great amounts of heat can be drawn from their surfaces.

Turning Food into Motion

All this elaborate machinery is needed by the bird to release energy and raw materials from its food. But how did energy get into the food in the first place? There's still much to be learned, but this we do know: all the energy in food originally comes from the sun.

This energy first gets "locked into" green plants during a remarkable and still not completely understood process called *photosynthesis* that takes place in the leaves of these plants. The sun's energy takes apart the atoms in water from the ground and carbon dioxide from the air and puts some of them back together into a form of sugar called *glucose*. The plant draws up other materials along with the water from the ground. When all this rearranging of materials is finished, much of the light energy that struck the plant is trapped within it, holding these new sugar molecules together. They now become the basic food for all living things—every plant and every animal on our earth. Even the plant that helped put this food together must use some of it for its own life and growth.

To get the energy back out of the food, the whole process is reversed. The food is burned in every cell, which is photosynthesis in reverse. Atoms in the food are rearranged, with oxygen, back into water and carbon dioxide, plus a substance called *ATP* (adenosine triphosphate). The water and carbon dioxide are dumped out of the cells as waste, but most of the sun's energy is still locked in the ATP molecule. It is in this form that energy is neatly concentrated for living things, ready to be released by the cells the moment it is needed.

The muscle cells that power the wings of birds use this ATP for their movement. Part of each muscle cell manufactures ATP as it burns food; another part of the same cell uses ATP as its energy source. When a muscle is at rest, an automatic brake prevents any of this ATP from releasing its energy. But if the muscle cell is stimulated, these brakes are removed and the ATP releases its energy, causing each muscle cell to contract. As bundles of these muscle cells contract, the wings of the bird move.

The blazing sun provides energy for all living things. It keeps our planet warm enough for life to exist here. It makes the air rise and the winds blow so that graceful gliding birds can soar easily above our heads. And through the green plants that contain tiny bits of its energy, the sun powers even the flying machinery of every bird.

Chapter 9

VARIETY OF FLIGHT

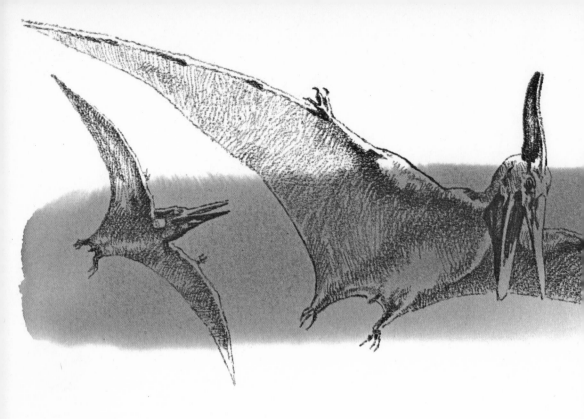

It TOOK millions and millions of years for flying animals to evolve. In the millions of years that have passed since then, these flying animals have spread to every part of our earth, and have made themselves at home in whatever environment they've found. They have developed adaptations to the heat of the jungle, to the scarcity of water in the desert, to the cold of the ice-packs.

They swim and catch fish, they hunt and kill. They can fly over mountains or skim the surface of the water. They can fly backward and forward, or hover in the air. They glide and soar, flap and flutter. Some dive into the water from a hundred feet above it, some explode suddenly into the air from the tangle of a forest.

The earth is very large, and yet even the airy world of birds is crowded. Each bird must find a place for itself, and because there are so many different kinds of places, there are many, many different kinds of birds.

Variety in Size

Birds come in many sizes and weights. The largest and heaviest ones, of course, cannot fly: the African ostrich, the Australian emu, the New Guinea cassowary. The heaviest birds that can get off the ground are the great bustards of Europe and the Australian bustards, who weigh as much as thirty-two pounds.

Because birds are different sizes,

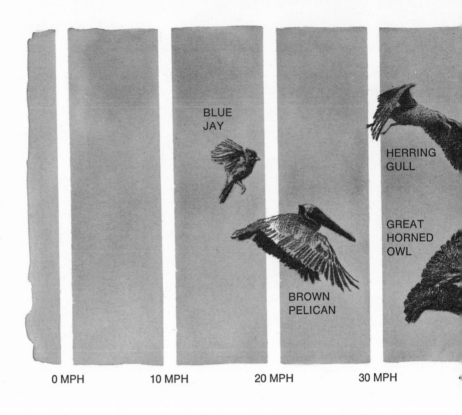

BLUE
JAY

HERRING
GULL

GREAT
HORNED
OWL

BROWN
PELICAN

0 MPH   10 MPH   20 MPH   30 MPH

they naturally have different-sized wings. The heavier the bird, the more lift it needs. This would seem simply to require larger wings, but birds do not always develop in this fashion. As a bird increases in size, its body grows in three directions: it gets longer and wider and thicker. The lifting surface of its wings, however, only gets longer and wider. So the amount of lift the wings can produce does not increase as rapidly as the load they must support. One rather unusual way around this loading problem is for a bird to evolve longer and longer wings without increasing the size of its body. The frigate is an extreme example: it is almost all wing, with just a tiny body hung in the middle.

Another problem with wings is that the larger they are, the more difficult they are to move. Except for gliding birds that take advantage of rising currents of air, most of the heavier birds with large wings have considerable difficulty flying, so they spend most of their lives not flying. For the smaller birds, however, flight is much easier,

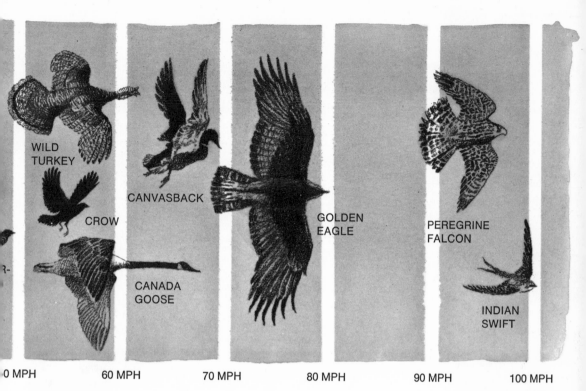

| 0 MPH | 60 MPH | 70 MPH | 80 MPH | 90 MPH | 100 MPH |

Just as man achieved his greatest speeds in the air, so too have other animals of the Wild Kingdom. Freed from the friction of land and water, some birds can fly incredible speeds—the peregrine falcon can fly at more than 100 mph, and dives at nearly 200 mph!

and they spend many of their waking hours flitting from place to place.

Variety in Speed

It is very difficult to tell accurately just how fast a bird can actually fly without knowing the speed and direction of the air around it. Suppose, for example, a bird can fly thirty miles an hour in perfectly still air. This would be called its air speed. But this particular bird on this particular day is being helped from behind by a fifteen mph tailwind. It would actually pass over forty-five miles of the earth's surface in an hour. This would be its ground speed. If the bird turned around so that same fifteen mph wind was now slowing it down, it would be able to cover only fifteen miles in an hour although its air speed would be thirty mph in both cases.

The top speed of a bird depends on its design, and this design is related to where the bird lives and how it gets its food. Generally, larger birds can fly

[115]

faster than smaller ones—but not always. Nor does the rate of its wingbeats tell much about a bird's top speed. A vulture may flap its wings only once a second, but these large wings create great amounts of lift and each stroke provides a powerful forward thrust. Smaller wings can and must be moved more rapidly. Small land birds flap their wings about fourteen times a second, and have air speeds of twenty-five miles an hour. The fastest wingbeats of all belong to the smallest birds. The giant hummingbird of the Andes moves its wings ten times a second; the smallest hummingbird flaps them at the incredible rate of eighty times a second! And some hummingbirds can dart through the air at sixty mph.

Each bird, of course, can fly at a number of speeds, depending upon whether it's out enjoying the view or is being chased by a hungry hawk. But each type of bird has a top speed beyond which it cannot fly. Its particular design determines its speed limit.

Any object that moves through the air meets resistance from it; the amount depends on the shape of the object. To keep moving, the bird or plane must overcome this resistance, or drag. The problem is that drag doesn't just increase directly as an object increases its speed, it multiplies. For example, if a bird doubles its speed, drag increases four times! At a certain speed the drag becomes so great that any further increases in speed are impossible. So the design of an object sets an absolute speed limit

on how fast it can move through air.

The fastest bird is probably the peregrine falcon, or duck hawk. With wings swept back like those of a jet, it can reach speeds of one hundred mph or better in level flight, and nearly two hundred mph in its famous power dive after prey. To achieve this speed, its wings are folded tightly back against its body, making it more missile-shaped than bird-shaped. Although birds, at least as presently designed, have fixed limits as to how fast they can fly, man-made ships can be designed differently, so their top speeds seem to be limited only by our imaginations.

Speed is only one part of flight. Depending on what a bird must do to survive, it may have different flight needs. For example, ruffed grouse, pheasants, and quail are all related; they're birds that spend most of their time on the ground. They find their food on the ground, they nest on the ground, and, in general, they rely on the special colors of their feathers to hide them from enemies. These colors blend in with the birds' surroundings, making them almost invisible. When danger approaches, they "freeze," so that movement won't give away their position. Flight is used only in emergencies when this technique fails. If these birds must fly, there is little room in their tangled environment for a

Exploding into air, a pheasant climbs almost straight up. If "flushed out" several times, the bird becomes so exhausted it is unable to fly at all, and can be captured by hand.

long, running takeoff. Instead, they catapult almost straight into the air, powered by short, broad wings.

If these birds are flushed out like this several times, they become exhausted and are unable to fly at all. The muscles that make these sudden bursts of speed and power possible aren't built for sustained flight. The breast muscles of these birds are white, which means there aren't many blood vessels running through them. Although this white meat may be good to eat, it does not have enough pathways to bring in great quantities of food and oxygen to replace that which is burned up in the bird's sudden explosion into the air. Birds like ducks, however,

Some wings are particularly effective in fast takeoffs.

have *red* flight muscles. These provide a fuel delivery system large enough for long, sustained flights.

Most birds, whether they fly a little or they fly a lot, carefully conserve their energy when they do fly. They do not often fly faster than they need to, just as we do not run if walking will do the job. And birds do not fly higher than they must, for enormous amounts

of energy are consumed climbing against gravity's pull. In addition, the air gets cooler the higher they go, so still more energy will be wasted just keeping warm. At higher altitudes, the air gets thinner, too, and provides less support for the wings, less oxygen for the lungs.

Variety in Maneuverability

Some birds can make incredibly sharp turns at top speed. Others cannot steer very well at all and generally keep flying in a fairly straight line. The difference is in the design of the tail: birds and planes and boats all change their direction in much the same way. A boat has a rudder behind it that is bent against the moving water. Depending on which way the rudder is turned, it gets bumped harder on one side than on the other. This swings the back of the boat around so the front faces a new direction. A plane is turned in the same way by bending the back half of its vertical stabilizer against the moving air.

A bird uses its tail in exactly the same way. That is, if the tail is made of broad, stiff flight feathers that can be opened or closed like a fan, moved up or down, and twisted to the right or left. When a bird wants to turn left, it bends its tail left. Air striking against the tail swings the back of the bird to the right. Now the front of the bird is facing the new direction.

Actually, turning involves more than this for airborne objects. Birds and planes bank as they turn. That is, they tilt one wing up higher than the other. They do this for the same reason engineers bank the curves of a highway: it prevents skidding. Banking is extremely important for birds and planes because they don't have a road to hang onto. If they turn without banking, their bodies tend to keep moving straight ahead even though they are now facing and flying in a different direction. This, of course, is a skid. Banking braces the whole underside of the bird's wings and body against the oncoming air—and so reduces the amount of skidding.

There are other techniques for turning. Some birds are able to beat one wing a little faster than the other, which has the same effect as pulling harder on one oar of a rowboat. The side of the bird receiving more power tends to move ahead of the other side, and the bird turns in the direction of the slower-moving side.

Steering up and down is done with the bird's tail in much the same way that it's done with the horizontal tail of an airplane. The tail is bent in the

Differently designed wings are required for high speeds.

opposite direction from that in which the bird wants to go.

Gliding and soaring birds have evolved wings quite different from those of the more active flyers. In

Long, broad wings are used by the long-distance fliers.

general, they're larger than wings that must be moved quickly. It is interesting to note, however, two completely different designs that have evolved to do the same job. Soaring birds that live over land (such as eagles and condors and hawks) have broad, slotted wings. The sea birds that specialize in soaring (like the albatrosses) have long, narrow wings. Why these two different designs evolved no one knows. Which is best no one can say, for both kinds of soaring birds have been extremely well designed.

Diving Birds

Life began in the sea, evolved into many different forms, including fish, and eventually moved onto the land. Some of these land animals learned to fly, some of them returned to the sea.

It took millions of years for swimming creatures to evolve into flying animals. Now some birds have returned to the sea.

Whales and porpoises are mammals whose ancestors once lived on land. Penguins are descendants of birds who once flew.

This transition back to the sea is not complete. Although whales and porpoises still breathe air, they can't leave the water; penguins can still waddle awkwardly over the land or toboggan down the ice on their stomachs, but are most at home in the water. The wings of penguins have evolved into finlike devices, but the bird ancestry of these animals still shows plainly. Penguins do not swim in the same way fish do, with snakelike movements of the body and tail. Instead, penguins use their flipper-like wings to move through the water in very much the same way other birds use them to move through the air—and at nearly the same speeds.

Flight demands lightness, but birds that swim underwater cannot be too light or they would bob up to the surface like a piece of cork. Emperor penguins, at a hefty ninety pounds, are too heavy for flight, but they have no trouble staying submerged. They even carry stones in their stomachs, which may be ballast to help keep them underwater. These stones do not seem to be needed for digestion; penguins are not seed-eaters, they live on fish. Their thick layers of fat also add to their weight, but, more importantly, protect them from heat loss in their frigid homes. And it is cold where they live: emperors hatch eggs in temperatures as low as eighty degrees Fahrenheit below zero!

Living in both air and water presents certain vision problems for penguins. Since these birds hunt for fish, their greatest need is for sharp underwater vision. So the lenses in their eyes are focused primarily for underwater viewing. But penguins are not able to change the focus of their eyes as easily as most other birds. When they leave the water, the focus does not correct itself, so on land penguins are very, very near-sighted.

There are many in-between animals in the Wild Kingdom. Grebes, loons, auks, and puffins are other birds that spend most of their time in the water. But unlike penguins, these birds can fly if absolutely necessary. Getting up into the air is difficult for them, but they are strong, swift flyers once they do get up. Their feet trail far behind them when they fly, and are used instead of the tail for steering. Underwater, these legs do the propelling, and they're located in about the same position as the propeller of a boat. Swimming underwater presents the same problem to these birds as it does to any other air-breathing animal. How can a loon stay submerged for fifteen minutes? What does a penguin do for air? Scientists have discovered that the moment any animal dives under-

With its feet kicking behind it like the propeller of a submarine, a loon speeds through the water after its dinner.

water, its heart rate and oxygen consumption automatically slow down. So whatever supply of oxygen these diving birds take down with them lasts longer than might otherwise be expected.

Sea Birds

When we think of the great variety of birds, we sometimes forget there are birds that spend almost all their lives at sea. These birds find everything they need in the oceans' waters, except a safe place to build a nest for their eggs. For this they must return to land. But once nesting is finished, a bird like the huge wandering albatross may leave its island breeding ground and roam the oceans of the earth for several years, seldom approaching land. It feeds on seafood and can drink the salty water of the sea that would kill most other animals. It can glide endlessly and effortlessly on the strong ocean breezes, and gently settle down to rest on the surface of the water. Albatrosses, shearwaters, and petrels are perhaps the best known of the true ocean birds.

GULL

There are other birds that live along the coasts: gulls, terns, cormorants, and pelicans. These birds have turned to the sea as their source of food, but are never really found too far from land. Whatever the differences between the true ocean birds and the coastal ones, there are certain problems common to them all.

First of all, there is the problem of food. The basic food for all the sea's creatures are microscopic plants and animals called *plankton,* which float near the surface of the water. The tiny green plants of the plankton capture the sun's energy in exactly the same way as the green plants of the land. Where there is a lot of plankton, there will be a lot of fish. Where there are many fish, there will be many birds to

CORMORANT

TERN

PELICAN

The gull, the cormorant, the tern and the pelican all get their food from the water, but seldom venture very far from land.

feed on them. Sometimes the nests of these birds will be very close to the food supply; coastal birds can often see their nests while they hunt for food. But the true sea birds may travel hundreds and sometimes thousands of miles between visits to their nests.

If sea birds had to exert energy constantly to stay above the water, they would quickly burn up their food. But the winds of the oceans blow almost continually, and so these great birds conserve their energy by gliding and dynamic soaring. If there is no wind and the birds are weighted down with food, they may not be able to rise from the water until another breeze comes along to help. Too little wind, therefore, can become a problem. It is more of a problem actually than too much wind, for even a hurricane is no danger to sea birds unless it dashes them against the land. At open sea, they can ride out almost any storm.

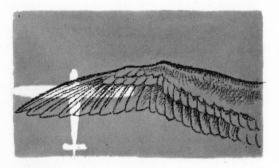

Gliding sea birds and gliders both have long, narrow wings.

But there is a water problem at sea for many animals. A man would soon die of thirst at sea even with an oceanful of it around him. If he drinks sea water, its high concentration of salt soon dehydrates his body. Most animals cannot drink salt water. But special nasal glands have evolved in ocean birds that quickly remove any extra salt from their bodies and prevent the salt concentration from rising to a dangerous level.

There is also a problem keeping dry at sea. Gannets and gooneys have heavily oiled, waterproof feathers; they do not mind even sleeping on the water. But man o' wars and cormorants have loose feathers that get wet easily, so these birds spend as much time as they can on land or in the air, and get into the water only when fishing.

This fishing is done in many different ways. Some birds just skim the surface of the water looking for food. But the creatures in some parts of the sea are not always swimming close to the surface, so other birds must dive after them. The extreme lightness of these birds—perfect for flying—causes a problem in diving. To overcome the buoyancy of the water, some birds must first fly thirty to one hundred feet above it, then make a spectacular plunge down into it after their food.

Diving into water without getting hurt requires skill, as anyone knows who has done a belly flop against its hard surface. Different birds have worked out different ways to get into the water. Ospreys and pelicans fly along until they spot their prey. They can do this from great heights. Then they bank their wings sharply to eliminate lift, just as planes do when they "peel off" for a dive. With lift gone, gravity pulls them down, and they plummet toward the water, wings partly open to control their speed and direction.

The osprey uses its feet to strike the fish, so just before entering the water its feet shoot out past its head, and the animal disappears in a spray of water. A moment later it reappears, and with wings sweeping back and forth horizontally, it rises almost straight up like a helicopter until it's clear of the water. Then the wings switch to a vertical motion and the bird is on its way.

The pelican, on the other hand, hits the water headfirst. It spirals down, crashes into the water, and scoops the fish up in its remarkably elastic pouch. As it pops above the surface again, it faces the wind for extra lift, drains the pouch of perhaps a gallon of water, and quickly takes off before a gull or some other bird snatches the meal away from it.

A special design modification makes it possible for diving birds to make these spectacular takeoffs with soaking wet feathers. The ends of the flight feathers are notched. This prevents the birds' slots from getting stuck when they are wet and failing to open during the critical takeoff.

Probably the most extreme variation in flight technique belongs to the hummingbird, famous for being the smallest of all birds and for its ability to hover in the air for long periods of time. Although there are other birds that can hover, there is no bird smaller than the smallest hummingbird. There is no mammal smaller either. The bee hummingbird weighs no more than an American nickel, is not any bigger than a bumblebee, and is probably the smallest size that a warm-blooded creature can be. Any animal smaller would not be able to eat fast enough to maintain its temperature—and would die.

GREBE

AUK

PUFFIN

Though they may live far from one another, auks, puffins and grebes are all at home in and around water.

A

B

C

D

Flight presents a special problem for these small animals. The smaller the wing, the less lift it produces. So the smaller the bird, the faster its wings must beat to make up for this. A bird the size of a bumblebee is aerodynamically more like an insect than a bird, and its inefficient wings must move at insect-like speeds. The smallest hummingbird moves its wings back and forth eighty times a second, and in many respects its flight techniques are much more like those of insects than of birds.

Hummingbirds do not fly with their bodies in the same horizontal position as other birds, but keep them more upright. This means that their wings do not move up and down, but sweep back and forth, pushing air downward instead of backward. Each time the wings change direction, they also twist ninety degrees, so air is pushed downward whichever direction they move.

This works in much the same way as the horizontal rotor of a helicopter.

The hummingbird's wings produce almost as much power on their forward sweep, or upstroke, as on their return, so the wing muscles are developed accordingly. Quite unlike the muscles of most other birds, those that move the hummingbird's wings during the upstroke are almost as large as those that power the downstroke. Their combined weight accounts for a rather startling 30 per cent of a small hummingbird's total weight.

The variety in size and design of birds is enormous—or so it seems when you compare the tiny hummingbird with the giant ostrich. For all that, there is actually much less variation between different birds than between different mammals. The ostrich weighs 60,000 times more than the bee hummingbird, but the blue whale weighs 60,000,000 times more than the pigmy shrew.

A unique design allows helicopters and hummingbirds to hover. With body upright, the hovering hummingbird sweeps its wings forward (Positions A, B and C). This lifts the bird by pushing the air downward. As the wings change direction and begin to sweep back (D), they twist over and so can continue pushing the air downward.

Chapter 10

THE MYSTERY OF MIGRATION

BECAUSE birds can fly, they have moved easily into every portion of the earth—from the tropics to the polar regions, to every continent and almost every island. Because flight is such an efficient way of traveling, birds have been able to move farther in their search for food than any land-bound animals.

In the parts of our earth away from the equator, the seasons constantly change. Each year, spring gives way to summer, summer to fall, and fall to winter. The farther away from the equator, the more severe these winters are, and the harder they are on all living things. Freezing temperatures stop plants from growing, and they must wait almost lifelessly until the water they need for life unfreezes once again. Winter's bitter touch kills many insects and forces others to spin cocoons or bury themselves in the ground. The birds that depend on these insects for food find the winter's offerings slim.

Some birds switch from insects to the few things that are left in winter—berries and seeds and nuts. But even these foods are in short supply; there is simply not enough food available in winter to feed all the birds.

The problem is as simple as life itself: animals cannot live without food. The total amount of food available in any area puts an absolute limit on the number of animals that can live there. Each square mile of land in its natural state can support a limited number of plants, which, in turn, can support just so many insects and rodents, so many snakes, so many birds, and just so many larger mammals.

But flight makes it possible for birds to leave these areas where the food is in short supply. They do not have to stay and starve. So most of them leave, looking for food where the supply has not been reduced by winter's cold. As these yearly changes in the weather repeat themselves, so do the birds' journeys after food. This had led to a habit now millions of years old, a habit so dramatic and complicated it still defies complete explanation, a habit that allows many birds to enjoy the best of several possible worlds—the habit of migration.

Each year, hundreds of millions of birds take part in these massive flights. In spring they move from their wintering grounds to summer nesting homes; in fall they return. Since most of our earth's land is in the Northern Hemisphere, most migration takes place in the north. The closer a bird lives to the equator, the less reason there is for

it to migrate. More birds migrate from Canada than from the United States, and more from the United States than from Mexico. In the tropics, there is little migration at all.

Most of these seasonal journeys, then, take the birds from one climate zone to another. Because our earth is tipped toward the sun the way it is, the climate zones run around our earth in bands parallel to the equator. So most of these flights are north or south journeys across these bands. But not all of them. Sometimes the wet and dry seasons affect the supply of food and force birds to migrate; these flights might be in easterly or westerly directions. And some migrations are up and down! A number of birds manage to change climates without taking long trips. They simply move down the mountainside when winter freezes out their food, and move back up when spring returns. A three-mile trip down into a valley can sometimes produce as dramatic a climate change as a 5,000-mile trip south.

But shortages of food are not always caused by weather. Sometimes the animal population increases until there are too many animals for the available plant food. Competition for food becomes fiercer and many of the animals are driven out of the area. Overpopulation and lack of food are obvious reasons why animals would migrate. But what accounts for birds that leave on their journeys long before there is any actual shortage of food?

Perhaps part of our difficulty in understanding some of the things that are happening today is that the original causes for them may no longer exist. The reasons that certain birds fly certain routes may have disappeared a long time ago, but the urge and the ability to migrate are still passed on from generation to generation. We can only guess how it all began.

Original Causes of Migration

For years it was commonly accepted that birds must have originated in the north, and then were driven south by the first great ice sheet that swept down from the pole. When this icecap receded, the birds worked their way back up to the nesting grounds of their ancestors. Three more ice sheets moved down and then receded. This rhythm became a pattern for the birds to follow, and many of them are still doing it today. That's one theory.

Another theory suggests that almost the opposite thing might have happened. Suppose birds didn't originate in the north, but rather in the tropics. In the mild climates there, life was very good and the birds multiplied. But the very ease with which they could live and multiply eventually led to overcrowding. This forced some of the birds to move farther and farther in all directions looking for more room to live.

Those birds that moved beyond the equator found more hours of daylight to search for food during the nesting season. Since this is the time they must get food not only for themselves but for their brood as well, the extra hours of daylight would have been an important advantage in their successful survival. Most of the earth's land is northward, so the birds continued moving northward. The farther north they breed, the longer the summer days are for nesting—and the larger their broods actually are!

Which of these theories is right? Is either one correct? Or is there another and better explanation? Perhaps there were many reasons for birds to begin migrating rather than just one great cause. Piecing together the past is difficult. For every likely explanation, there is usually an equally reasonable counterexplanation. But whatever the original causes, this we do know: a bird is born with the urge to migrate or not migrate.

In some birds, the inborn drive to migrate is so strong that, when the time comes to start, a mother may leave her helpless young behind. Yet other birds of the same species may not migrate at all. Experiments show that not only is the urge to migrate passed on from generation to generation, but so is most of the other information birds need to make spectacular journeys. They seem to know when to start, what route to follow, where they're going, and what time to start back on the return journey. They don't have to be taught these things, they know them instinctively. They don't have to follow older birds who have made the trip before; they are born with the route somehow imbedded within them.

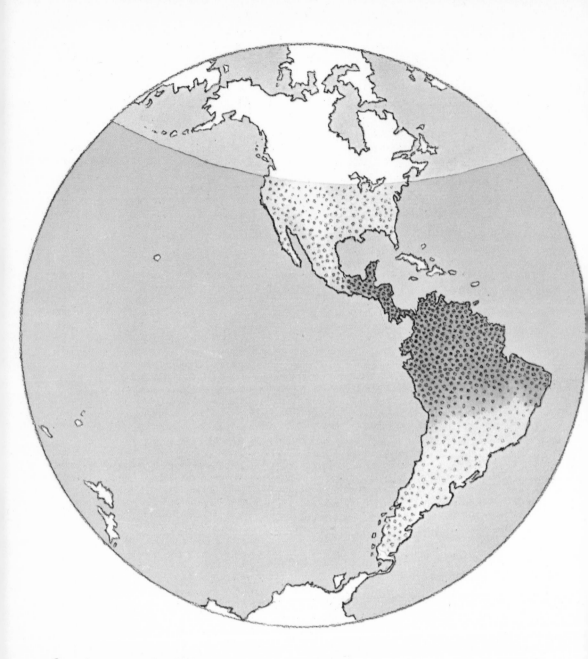

One theory says that birds originated in the Northern Hemisphere and the great ice sheets forced them south. When the ice retreated, descendants of these birds moved back north and the pattern of migration was established.

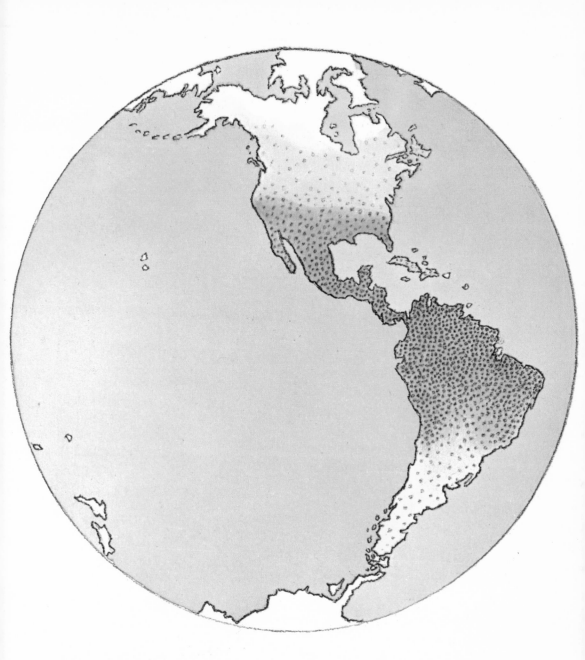

Other theories believe birds originated in the Southern Hemisphere. Gentle climate and abundant food helped them multiply until the land became overcrowded. Many were then forced northward looking for room in which to live.

These instincts, or urges, are passed on to birds in the very way their bodies grow—from that single first cell. If it seems fantastic to us that a tiny cell could contain such elaborate messages as when to start migrating and how to get there, consider all the other information a cell contains. Think of the cell that divides and redivides to become an intricate feather, another that becomes the bird's eyes, another its talons, still another its muscles. Instructions for all this are passed on along with information about migration.

We don't know yet exactly how these coded messages are transmitted by the cells, but we can marvel at their precision; the details of migration are as complicated as the design of a feather. Unless severe storms or unusual weather conditions interfere, some birds make trips that cover thousands of miles and arrive at their destination the same week year after year.

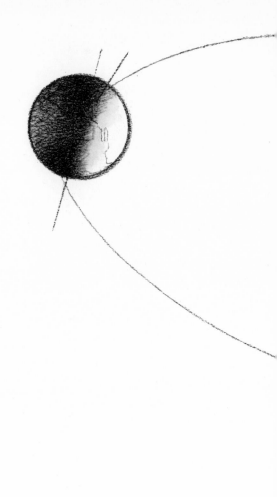

The Triggering Mechanism

Scientists have tried for a long time to discover how birds know when to begin migrating. Their studies show that weather conditions play some part, but just what it is no one really knows. A warm air mass from the south early in spring does bring thousands of migrating birds with it. More than likely, birds do take advantage of favorable wind conditions. But something more precise than the changeable weather triggers migration, some clock more accurate than a warm spring day tells birds when to begin.

Scientists began to look inside birds for some "internal clock" that signaled the start of migration. They found that certain glands were more active in some birds just before migration time. These particular glands release hormones into the bloodstream that speed up the energy output of the whole system. This might explain some of the remarkably strenuous flights of migrating birds. But the picture isn't clear

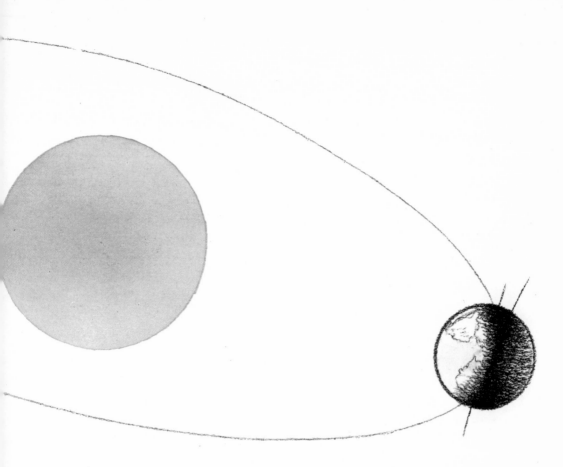

Because our earth is tipped slightly as it moves about the sun, sometimes one hemisphere and then the other receives more sunlight.

because all migrating birds don't have this hormone production.

Some birds put on weight just before migration; layers of fat accumulate on their bodies. Fat is stored energy that can be released when the bird is unable to eat—for example, over water. But again, the picture is confused because these changes are not found in all birds that migrate. And suppose it is these body changes that do trigger migration, what triggers the body changes? Since migrations are a yearly occur-

rence, perhaps the "internal clock" the scientists were looking for was really an "internal calendar." Perhaps birds are able to tell the time of year.

The seasons change here on earth because the axis of our planet is tipped slightly from the vertical; it's not absolutely straight up and down in relation to our orbit about the sun. This tipping causes first one part of the earth and then another to face the sun more directly as it slowly journeys about it. When the northern half faces the sun,

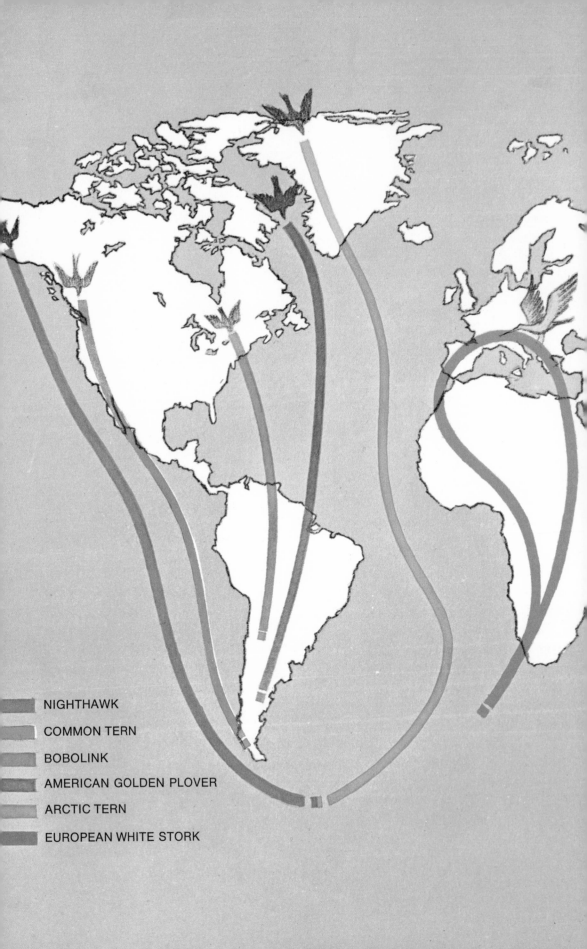

NIGHTHAWK

COMMON TERN

BOBOLINK

AMERICAN GOLDEN PLOVER

ARCTIC TERN

EUROPEAN WHITE STORK

the hours of sunshine there are very long—and it is summer. As the northern half tips away from the sun in fall and winter, the days get shorter and shorter.

In 1926, the Canadian biologist William Rowan reversed this effect on some caged experimental birds. In autumn, he extended the shortening days with artificial lights, leaving them on longer and longer each day. He wanted to learn if birds used the changing hours of sunlight to tell them when to begin migrating. Could he fool these birds into behaving as if it were spring rather than fall? As the experiment continued, the birds grew restless, just as they normally do before migration. When released, half the birds that had received the extra light took off toward the north! Rowan had thrown their calendars off by six months. They flew north even though they were already north!

The experiment continued. Normally, after a bird arrives north, it builds its nest, lays its eggs, and raises its young. Did Rowan's birds show any changes in their reproductive organs as a result of the additional light? They did. These organs increased in size as much as a hundred to a thousand times when the bird was exposed to longer hours of light. When the light was decreased, these glands grew smaller again. This suggested that it is the increasing daylight of spring that causes internal changes in a bird—and these changes in turn trigger the start of its northern migration.

The Magnitude of the Mystery

When winter chills one environment, birds migrate to another. They try to keep the living conditions about them comfortably the same. It is not at all surprising, then, that they tend to migrate between areas that are very much alike. Birds that live in a wooded area in the north fly to a similar wooded area in the south; shore birds will exchange one shore for another. To do this, some birds need fly only very short routes, while others must migrate enormous distances. Those with long journeys ahead of them start early. Usually, the last birds to leave in fall are just making a short trip south; they will also be the first to return in spring. These limited migrations don't puzzle us much, but some of the longer ones are very hard to understand.

For example, during the winter the great shearwaters live all over the Atlantic Ocean. But when spring breeding-time comes, they return by the millions to a small group of islands in the middle of the southern Atlantic,

SHEARWATER

Tristan da Cunha, 1,500 miles from either Africa or South America. From end to end, these islands are less than thirty miles long. Yet the shearwaters somehow make it back to these tiny islands from wherever they have wandered.

The American golden plover is another example of remarkable navigation over water. These birds nest in northern Canada. In fall, young plovers fly an inland route south. They fly over the United States, Mexico, Central and South America to get to their winter homes in southern Brazil and Argentina. The older birds, however, take a more direct route; their trip south includes a more than 2,000-mile stretch over the open Atlantic Ocean.

AMERICAN GOLDEN PLOVER

Water presents a problem for some migrating birds and doesn't bother others at all. The large European white storks avoid flights over water whenever they can. In fact, these storks take two completely different routes to avoid water. Which land route they fly to Africa in the fall depends on where they've nested dur-

ing the summer. The western European storks, for example, follow a western route south through Spain. They cross the Mediterranean at its narrowest point, the Strait of Gibraltar, then fly on down the western coast of Africa.

The storks that nest in eastern Europe follow an eastern route, avoiding large bodies of water with equal care. They do fly over the tip of the Bosporus Sea, but from there on the migration is essentially over land. They fly across Turkey, carefully skirting the eastern edge of the Mediterranean as they fly into Africa. These eastern European storks settle for the winter all down the eastern half of the African continent. The storks that live in between have a choice. Some of the birds that live in central Europe take the eastern route, others the western one. It has even been reported that two birds from the very same nest have taken off along different routes!

EUROPEAN WHITE STORK

Terns are famous flyers and are distantly related to gulls. The beautiful common tern nests along the eastern coast of North America and migrates an enormous distance to its winter home at the southernmost tip of South

ARCTIC TERN

COMMON TERN

America. But the most extraordinary migration of all is that of the Arctic tern. This bird is about seventeen inches long and some nest within ten degrees of the North Pole. During their summer nesting period, the terns enjoy almost continuous sunshine—for this is the land of the midnight sun. Late in August, the terns leave their cold northern home and follow the sun in its southern journey across the sky.

One group flies along the west coast of Africa, crosses the equator, and continues to the frozen ice packs of Antarctica. It arrives on the opposite side of the earth in time to enjoy three months of almost continuous sunshine down there—after a trip of some 11,000 miles! When the sun returns

north, the bird flies another 11,000 miles to return with it, bringing its yearly travels to 22,000 miles! With this system, the Arctic tern holds the mileage record for travel, and probably enjoys more hours of daylight every year than any other creature in the Wild Kingdom—perhaps eight months of continuous sunshine in some cases. But the effort expended to make such a trip is so extreme that a number of other arctic birds do not bother

BOBOLINK

migrating at all. They apparently have found it as easy to adapt somehow to the hardships of the arctic winter as it is to make the 22,000-mile trip.

The distance birds migrate doesn't seem to be limited by their size. The bobolink is smaller than an American robin and travels nearly 7,000 miles each way in its migrations. The longest trip of any North American land bird is made by the nighthawk, a bird only about ten inches long. Even the tiny ruby-throated hummingbird is capable of enormous flights—it migrates 3,000 miles every spring and fall. These small birds are able to make a five-hundred-mile, nonstop, overnight flight across the Gulf of Mexico—without refueling. To supply energy for such a trip, the hummingbird may burn up 25 per cent of its body weight.

It is remarkable statistics like these that make the mystery of migration so intriguing. Knowing the incredible distances involved and the precision with which the birds find their way from place to place increases our appreciation of the navigational skills that must be involved. How do birds find their way?

NIGHTHAWK

The Tumbling Pigeons

Since ancient times, men have known about the ability of some birds to find their way back to their roost, even when carried many miles away. Homing pigeons are the most famous of these birds, but experiments have shown that many other birds can "home" as well. For example, a Manx shearwater was taken from its breeding island near England and carried by plane to Boston, Massachusetts. Released, it was back home in less than two weeks. To our eyes, one seemingly endless expanse of water looks just like another, yet this bird was able to find its way back across the ocean. What landmarks on the water could

RUBY-THROATED HUMMINGBIRD

the bird possibly use? Or if not landmarks, what?

One theory put forward suggested that homing pigeons and other birds could "remember" exactly the way they'd come. When it was time for the return trip, they could retrace every turn of that route in reverse order. Perhaps the ability of other birds to navigate on long migration trips was just an extension of this technique.

To see if this were true, experimental birds were put to sleep with drugs, so they could not remember. While still unconscious, they were moved a great distance by the experimenter. Later, when they woke, they were released—and they found their way back home as accurately as control birds that hadn't been drugged. If this retracement theory had been correct, the recording mechanisms of these birds would have had to have been operating even when the birds were asleep. So the experimenters tried another method to test the theory.

They placed some homing pigeons in a large, lightproof drum, so the birds couldn't see where they were going. To confuse them further, the drum was placed on a turntable that revolved about four times a minute. Every time the truck carrying the birds turned a corner on its way to the release point, the drum tended to slow down—so the revolutions were uneven in speed. All in all, the birds had a most complicated series of turns to remember if this was indeed the method they used in homing. But none of this confused them; the birds returned to their roosts just as successfully as ones that had not been tumbled in the drum.

Many kinds of experiments have been used to try to find out how birds navigate. In Germany, Werner Ruppell trapped a large number of hooded crows as they passed northward during their spring migration. These birds were moved by train hundreds of miles west of the route they had been flying, then were released.

The results were extraordinary. The birds took off in the same compass direction they had been flying before, continuing in a path parallel to their normal migration route. Equally remarkable, they continued flying about the same distance they would have if their flight hadn't been interrupted. They ended their journeys just about the same number of miles north as they normally did. But because they had been moved west by the experimenter, they ended up west of their normal breeding grounds—and by just about the same number of miles as they'd been displaced by the train ride.

This new location for their breeding ground did not seem to bother the birds. They nested there during the summer, and in fall migrated back south in the same direction and distance as always. But because their route had been moved from its normal position during the original experiment, these birds wound up in a new location for their wintering grounds as well. But this did not bother them either, and they readily adapted to another new home.

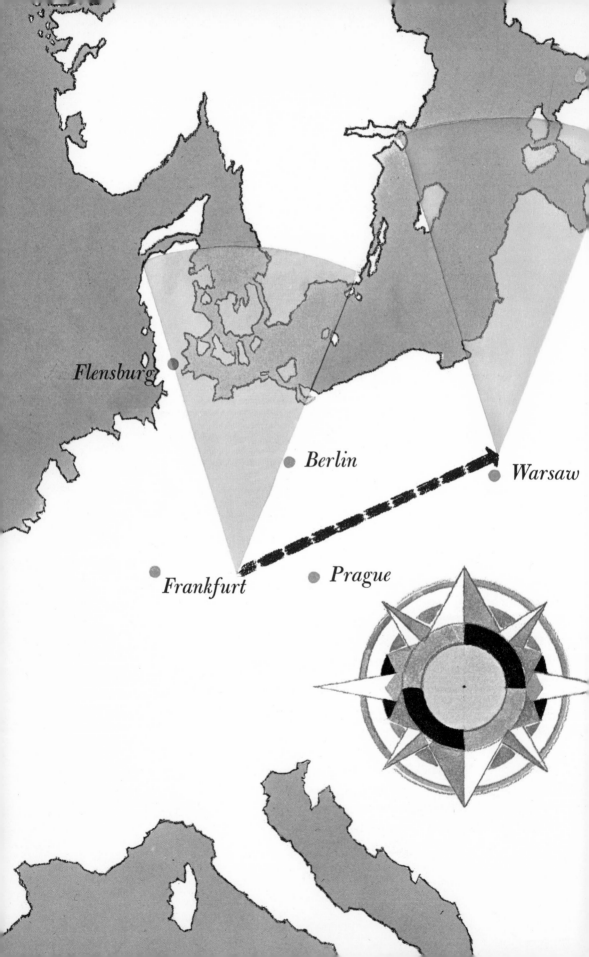

Ruppell's experiment suggested that these birds were equipped to fly in a certain compass direction when it was time to migrate. Moving them did not affect the direction of the urge at all. In addition, it appeared that they must have some kind of internal counting or timing or measuring device that tells them to stop when they have flown far enough to reach their traditional homes. Were the birds born with this information, or had they learned it from older birds?

Another experiment was set up. This time, very young birds were used, birds that had never migrated before. Even eggs were used. The eggs and the young birds were transported to a new area. Here the eggs were hatched and the young birds raised. In the fall, to make sure these young birds could not possibly follow any other birds that happened to be migrating through the area, they were held until all other birds had passed. In spite of all these controls, when these birds were finally released, they flew off in exactly the same direction as other birds of their species. The instinct to migrate in a certain direction is contained in the very egg from which the bird hatches.

Other experiments point to the same conclusion: birds are hatched with

Moved hundreds of miles off their normal route, migrating birds continued to fly the same compass direction when released.

some sort of direction-pointing mechanism inside them. If caged during their normal period of migration, birds become restless and move about the cage —but face most often the direction they would fly if they were free to migrate. Not only is the directional sense inborn, but so is the timing device that tells the birds when to stop flying. For the caged birds will show this exaggerated activity for only the length of time they'd normally be flying. Then whatever it is that was exciting them seems to run out, and the birds quiet down in their cages.

Strangely enough, the results of moving older birds from their normal routes were quite different from the results of moving young ones. Birds that had made the trip before seemed able to make flight corrections to get back to their normal winter and summer homes. They were apparently able to turn off these automatic compass and timing mechanisms and find their way back to the areas they knew from earlier migrations.

Navigation by the Sun

Having a built-in compass sounds fine, but what makes it operate? The magnetized needle of an ordinary compass swings in the general direction of north because the earth itself is a giant magnet that affects the smaller one. Before that needle can do you any good as a direction finder, however,

In order to use the sun to tell directions, a bird must take into account the sun's movement across the sky from sunrise to sunset. To do this, it must have some sort of internal clock that tells it how long it has been since daybreak.

Wyou have to be able to see it. You have no way of telling which way is north or south in complete darkness.

But if you go outside on a sunny day, then perhaps you can tell directions even without a compass. For you know that the sun rises in one part of the sky, moves across it in an arc, and then sets on the opposite side. By using the position of the sun in the sky, you can find your way about, providing you make allowances for the time of day. You can't use the sun to give directions unless you know how much time has passed since sunrise. Telling direction by the sun requires two different pieces of information: you must know the position of the sun in the sky, and, in addition, you must know the time of day.

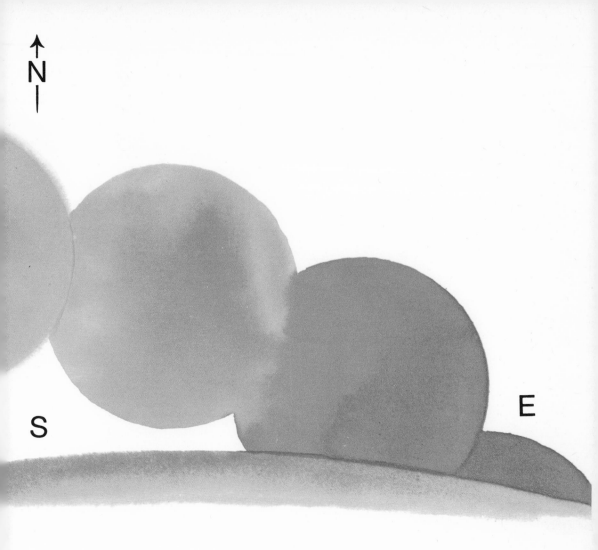

Men mastered this technique centuries ago, but it was only recently that someone wondered if perhaps birds navigated in this way. In 1949, a German scientist, Gustave Kramer, conducted experiments to find out. He knew that, during their migration periods, caged birds are restless. Repeated tests by Kramer with starlings showed that one bird tended to hop back and forth in the cage in the direction it would normally be flying. This orientation took place only on clear sunny days! If the sky was overcast and the sun hidden by clouds, there was absolutely no preference in the way the bird faced in its cage. When the sun came out again, the bird again lined up in a single direction. This suggested that this particular bird could tell the position of the sun and the time of day.

Kramer then began closing the windows of this specially constructed cage. The bird was still able to orient itself as long as at least one window was open. When all the windows were closed so that the bird had no view of the sky, it lost its sense of direction.

Kramer then put up large mirrors outside the windows of the testing cage, which made the sun appear to be about ninety degrees from where it actually was. This confused the bird's navigational mechanism: for the appropriate hour of day, the sun was not in the right position. To the bird this may have meant it was off course and facing in the wrong direction—so it swung around ninety degrees in its cage. Later experiments with more starlings seemed to confirm their ability to navigate by the sun.

Navigation by the Stars

But what about the many, many birds that migrate at night? The sun isn't any use to them as a directional guide. The night skies in spring and fall are filled with these smaller and more timid birds who prefer the protective covering of darkness. Actually, there are more night migrants than day travelers, for most birds need the daylight hours for feeding. How do these night travelers find their way between nesting and wintering grounds?

Until 1956, there was little information about night-migrating birds. But then another German ornithologist, Dr. Franz Sauer, set up an intriguing experiment. He used European warblers in cages that were glass-topped so the night sky was visible to them. At their normal time for migrating in the fall, the birds became restless. If the starry sky was visible, they took positions facing their customary migration destination. But if their view of the stars was blocked, they were confused about direction in the same way the day-flying birds were confused when the sun was hidden from them.

These same birds were then taken to a planetarium, a darkened chamber in which star patterns can be projected on a domed ceiling. The elaborate instrument was set to reproduce stars in exactly the same pattern as they appeared over Germany during the birds' fall migration. Under this artificial sky, the birds flapped their wings and pointed toward their winter home in Africa just as they had under the *real* sky. But when the star pattern on the ceiling was changed, the birds changed their positions in the cages accordingly, so they would still presumably be on a course toward Africa. The birds were navigating by the stars!

Because of the startling implications of this, researchers in different parts of the world are checking this experiment. Navigation by the stars is even more complicated than navigation by the sun. To do it, a bird needs a map of the constellations in its head that can be changed depending on the time of year and where the bird happens to be.

So far, other experiments, including radar observations, seem to confirm the ability of birds to navigate by the stars. Bouncing radio signals from the dark sky detects flocks of smaller birds and even some of the individual larger birds. These radar observations show that birds fly confidently on *starry* nights, but become confused about direction on *cloudy* nights when the stars aren't visible.

The full story of migration obviously cannot be told, for no one knows it yet. The more we learn about it, the more remarkable the real explanation will need to be. Meanwhile, the collection of theories grows, and if we haven't the right answer yet, it isn't because we lack imagination.

Other Explanations

Many proposed explanations involve special senses the birds might have. We know dogs and other animals have highly developed senses of smell that they use in direction finding. Perhaps birds have some additional sense beyond those five that we know about: hearing, sight, touch, taste, and smell. One theory suggests birds might be able to sense infrared heat waves, and that they find their way from place to place by reading these radiations from the earth.

A still more complicated theory suggests that birds are able to detect the earth's magnetic field and use this to find their way. But to navigate with a magnetic compass, the bird must be able to adjust it to the constantly vary-ing strength of the earth's field. In addition, these magnetic lines of force run in just one general direction—north and south. The bird would need still another device for determining its east-west position.

Nevertheless, experiments have been conducted to see if there is anything to this magnetic field theory. Small, permanent magnets have been attached to homing pigeons' heads, to the tips of their wings, and hung from strings around their necks. The idea was that if birds really could sense the earth's magnetic field, a strong magnet near them would jam their sensing mechanisms. But the magnets had no effect on their ability to return home. And so the search goes on and on.

Migratory Routes

Migrating birds probably pass over every part of the Northern Hemisphere, for there are about 100 billion birds on earth—and many of them are making round trips each year from north to south. Most often these flights are the most direct routes between the bird's breeding ground and its wintering home. But oceans, mountains, rivers, and lakes *do* have an influence on these flights, bending them this way and that.

In North America, four so-called *flyways* have been identified in which traffic is particularly heavy. Two of these routes follow the coastlines of the continent and are undoubtedly influenced by the ranges of mountains at either edge of our country. Another flyway cuts across the Great Plains. Perhaps the busiest of all is the one that follows the great Mississippi River Valley. Food and water are plentiful along this entire route, surely one of the reasons so many birds fly over it during their long-distance travels.

Are these migration routes ageless and unchanging? Apparently not, for within the very short history of the United States, migration routes have moved westward as men have moved westward. Robins that no longer migrate have overcome an old but powerful instinct. These instincts run deep, for even some birds that can't fly still migrate. Adelie penguins travel hundreds of miles between their winter and summer homes. They swim part of the way, then walk the rest of the way across the ice.

Today, new experiments and new techniques try to give us new insights into the mechanisms of migration. Some of the incredibly small devices being designed for space exploration are being borrowed. Miniaturized radio transmitters strapped to a bird will give us additional pieces of information. Devices that tell when the sun is visible to a migrating bird will automatically radio this information back to ground stations. Satellites will trace the patterns of bird migrations.

The story is complicated. Each year, millions of these birds fail to reach their destinations. Rain and snow and windstorms are the biggest killers; they blow the birds hundreds of miles off course or out to sea, or force them

down into the water. Many birds are dashed against buildings and television towers and airport beacons. In spite of the casualties, most birds *do* make it year after year. They fill the night skies with the soft flapping of their wings and the days with their songs. It's the mystery of just *how* they do it that still taunts us.

The Miracle of Flight

What is there about the flight of birds that fascinates us? Surely it's more than just the fact that they were in the air before us—though that is partly it. And it is more than the grace and beauty of their flight, the perfection and simplicity of their design. It is more than just the scientific principles of flight that interests us—though that's partly it too. We like to know that the flight of a bird is somehow related to the flight of a jet and a rocket. But it is more than that.

The flight of birds is much more than a momentary flash of feathers against the sky that catches our attention briefly. For as we look at this tiny miracle, we finally begin to realize that

The geography of land and water forms four natural routes for birds flying over North America: between the Pacific Ocean and the Rockies, over the Great Plains, along the Mississippi River Valley, and along the Atlantic coast.

We may never know how some of these fragile creatures fly thousands of miles through the dark of night and locate a single nest in a single tree they had left the year before.

though it's just one part of the Wild Kingdom—that part touches every other part and so touches us.

If we are the kind of people who cannot hear a jet roar overhead without looking up to marvel at it, then we must wonder about the outstretched wings of the plane and ask ourselves just how they are related to the wings of a bird. We will hold out our own arms to see how much alike and how different they are from the wings of bird and planes.

The slow pounding of our hearts in the darkness will remind us of the frantic heartbeats of the tiny birds. And that will remind us of the struggle that it is for all warm-blooded animals to keep warm—and alive.

The buzzing of insects in summer will remind us that, when the insects first took to the air millions of years ago, it was only a matter of time until larger creatures like birds would take off after them. And we realize that each thing in the Wild Kingdom depends on something else.

When we look up at the sky and see a cloud pass briefly over the sun, we remember that water and air and sunshine become the sugar that is the food for all the living things of our earth. We realize that so many different things all seem to be related to one another: the tug of the earth on the moon and the sun and the wind and the flight of birds.

When we think of the creatures that live in the sea, we remember how they have changed over hundreds of millions of years into creatures that run across the land and into those that fly above our heads, filling all the living spaces of our planet.

We see the pattern of life that is woven from one thing to the other, from plant to animal, from fire to water to man—and we see the differences. And we know as surely as life has changed during these last two billion years that it is changing right now as we look at it. Small changes perhaps, but changes that will become more and more obvious as time goes on. And we wonder about all the things there are still to be seen, still to be experienced, still to be learned in the Wild Kingdom.

INDEX

Quail, 116–18

Radio transmitters, 150
Reduced baggage, 89
Reproductive system, 89, 139
Reptiles, 24
Retina, 94–95
Ring toss, 91–92
Robins, 150
Rods, in eyes, 95
Routes, migratory, 149–50
Rowan, William, 139
Rowboat, 54
Ruppell, Werner, 143–45

Sauer, Franz, 148
Sea, 20–22, 23. *See also* Water
Sea birds, 65, 119, 122–27. *See also* Diving birds; Water birds
Secondary feathers, 52, 54, 55, 57
Shearwaters, 122, 139–40, 142
Shrews, 127
Size (*See also* Weight; specific parts): variety in, 112–15
Skidding, 119
Skulls, 84
Sleep, and migration, 143
Slots, slotting, 40–41, 52, 70, 71, 75
Speed: and lift, 41; and takeoff, landing, 69ff.; variety in, 115–16
Stalling, 40
Starlings, 147–48
Stars, 148–49
Steam engine, 100
Stereoscopy, 94
Stomach, 105
Storks, 140
Strokes, flight, 56–60
Sugar, 106, 108
Sun, sunlight, 108, 109, 137–39, 145–48
Supercharging, 105
Swans, 53, 74

Tail, tail feathers, 54, 55, 75, 118–19
Takeoffs and landings, 68–76, 125
Telephone lines, seeing, 94
Temperature (cold, heat), 98–100, 101, 107, 118, 120–21; excess heat, 107–8; insulation, 49–50; and migration (*see* Migration)

Teratornis incredibilis, 80
Terns, 122, 123, 141
Tertiary feathers, 52, 54
Thermals, 64–65
Tin cans, and gravity experiments, 25–26, 30
Torpid state, 101
Toucan, 84
Trees: animals in, 24; landing on, 75–76
Tristan da Cunha, 140
Turning, 118–19

Updrafts, 64–65, 74, 75

Vacuum. *See* Lift
Vaned feathers, 49–54, 55–60
Vanes, 50, 51, 55
Variety of flight, 112–27
Vision, 89–95, 121
Vultures, 63, 116

Warmth. *See* Temperature
Wastes, 105
Water, 108–9, 124 (*See also* Sea); and Bernoulli's Principle, 37–38; cooling system, 108; gravity and, 24–27, 28, 30; and migration, 140ff.; skiing, 36
Water birds, 53, 71. *See also* Sea birds; specific birds
Waterproofing, 50, 124
Weather. *See* Temperature
Weight, 79–84ff.; and energy system, 100–1; and gravity, 26–31; lift and bird's, 41; variety in size, 112–15
Whales, 120, 127
Windows, sticking hands out of car, 37, 41
Winds, 65, 123–24; and migration, 136; and takeoffs, 70, 71, 74
Wings, 14, 112, 119 (*See also* Diving birds; Sea birds); and aerodynamic forces, 34ff., 38–41; construction of, 46–47; and gliding flight (*see* Gliding and soaring); and gravity (*see* Gravity); modification in size and construction, 80ff.; and powered flight, 44–60; and takeoff and landing, 69–70ff.
Winter. *See* Migration; Temperature
Woodcocks, 93

R. MARLIN PERKINS, the commentator and star of the weekly television program, "Wild Kingdom," is the Director of the world-famous St. Louis Zoological Gardens. His career began at this same St. Louis Zoo, where his first job was as a laborer—sweeping sidewalks and trimming hedges. He rose rapidly to become Curator of Reptiles, and was then offered the position as Curator of the zoo in Buffalo, New York. From Buffalo, he moved to Chicago, where he was the Director of the Lincoln Park Zoo.

His television career started in Chicago, where he was the star of the program, "Zoo Parade." After his return to St. Louis in 1962, when he became director of the zoo, he started "Wild Kingdom," a program that has won countless awards, including the coveted "Emmy."

RICHARD CROMER, the author of THE MIRACLE OF FLIGHT, has written many of the "Wild Kingdom" scripts. For many years, he has written and produced educational radio and television programs, and is at present devoting most of his energies to the production of educational films—most of them for use in classrooms.

Shortly after his graduation from the University of Illinois, Mr. Cromer won a Fulbright study grant and spent a year in The Netherlands. Upon his return, he met Don Meier, the producer of "Wild Kingdom," and became one of the original three writers of the show. THE MIRACLE OF FLIGHT is his second book.